The Business of Coaching

Workbook

The Business of Coaching Workbook

Step-by-Step Activities and Resource Guide

Dorcas Kelley

CLARITY IN ACTION
Salinas, California

Published by: Clarity In Action,
a division of Kelley-Naumchik Consulting L.L.C.

The Business of Coaching[SM] is a registered service mark
of Kelley-Naumchik Consulting L.L.C.

CLARITY IN ACTION
19250 Reavis Way
Salinas, California   93907-1352
(831) 663-5364
FAX: (831) 769-9035
EMAIL: info@clarityinaction.com

Visit our web site at: www.clarityinaction.com

10   9   8   7   6   5   4   3   2   1

Printed in the United States of America.

This workbook is dedicated to you, the courageous coach who has taken the leap into small business ownership. Welcome!

Contents

Introduction

To accomplish great things we must first dream,
then visualize, then plan...believe...act!

ALFRED A. MONTAPERT

When I began the process of starting my own business in 1993, I knew virtually nothing about self-employment. Having always been an employee, I was most familiar with paychecks, W-2s, and having my business and health insurance needs covered by my employer. For the first few years, my husband and I researched and fumbled our way through the ins-and-outs of establishing, managing, and growing our business. It was a steep learning curve, filled with surprises and discoveries and potholes. But my love of being self-employed and the challenge of nurturing a business kept me engaged and motivated.

The objective of this workbook, and the companion book – *The Business of Coaching* – is to provide you with much of the information and knowledge that we've gathered over the years. My goal is to help you navigate around the potholes and to smooth out the road to your small-business success.

How To Use This Workbook

This workbook contains step-by-step activities and resources for nearly all the subjects discussed in *The Business of Coaching*. For each chapter in the companion book, there is a chapter of activities and resources in this workbook.

It's helpful to first read the chapter in *The Business of Coaching*, and then apply your knowledge by working through the activities in this workbook. In addition, each chapter has a list of resources (print and web-based) to facilitate further research and learning.

On the following pages you will find a Coaching Practice Checklist that lists the major tasks involved in starting, managing, and growing a business. Use this checklist to help structure and organize your business start-up efforts. The elements are listed in the basic order in which they should be addressed, that is, set up the business, take care of the financials, and then start your marketing efforts.

Coaching Practice Checklist

Use this checklist to structure and organize your efforts to establish, manage, and grow your coaching practice. Not all businesses will need or want all of the items listed, nor is this list exhaustive. Review the checklist to determine which elements are applicable to your practice, and which items you've already completed.

Laying the Foundation

- [ ] Business name
- [ ] Business structure
    - Sole proprietorship
    - Partnership
    - Limited Liability Company (LLC)
    - S-Corporation
- [ ] Fictitious business name filing
- [ ] Employer identification number
- [ ] Business license(s)
- [ ] Seller or resale permit, and sales tax license
- [ ] Zoning restrictions
- [ ] Address, phone, and fax numbers
- [ ] Internet access
    - Internet connection hardware (modem, ISDN, cable, DSL, satellite)
    - Internet service provider
    - Email account
    - Domain name
    - Web-hosting service provider

Financial Matters

- ❑ Record-keeping process
- ❑ Budget
- ❑ Business accounts (checking, business credit card)
- ❑ Accounts Payable management
- ❑ Client invoicing process
- ❑ Client payment methods (check, credit card, barter)
- ❑ Business insurance
  - Business property
  - Business liability
  - Automobile
  - Business interruption
  - Health and disability
  - Errors and omissions
- ❑ Taxes
  - Business deductions
  - Estimated tax payments
  - 1099s
  - Self-employment tax
  - Annual tax return
- ❑ Retirement plans (SEP-IRA, Keogh)

Marketing and Communications

- [ ] Marketing plan
  - Self-assessment
  - Target market definition
  - Short-term business goals
  - Short-term action plan
  - Marketing activities
- [ ] Marketing materials
  - Elevator speech
  - Business card and logo
  - Brochures
  - Introduction letters
  - Fliers or information sheets
  - Web site
- [ ] Effective networking

Around the Office

- [ ] Successfully transitioning to self-employment
  - Work structure
  - Work schedule
  - Time management
  - Paperwork management and retention
  - Improving efficiency
  - Addressing procrastination
- [ ] Office equipment
  - Telephone and headset
  - Messaging
  - Personal computer
  - Printer and fax machine
  - Office ergonomics

Laying the Foundation

Well begun is half done.

HORACE

1: Naming Your Business

2: Which Business Structure?
- Sole Proprietorship
- Partnership
- Limited Liability Company (LLC)
- S-Corporation

3: More Government Hoops
- Fictitious Business Name
- Employer Identification Number
- Business Licenses
- Reseller's or Seller's Permit; Sales Tax License
- Zoning Requirements

4: Business Contact Information
- Street Address
- Business Phone Number
- Fax Number
- Internet Access
- Internet Service Providers
- Internet Connections
  - Analog Modem
  - ISDN
  - Cable
  - DSL
  - Satellite
- Email Account
- Domain Name
- Web Hosting

1
Naming Your Business

Finding a business name requires creativity, brainstorming, and free association. Keep an open mind when you go through these activities and remember that seemingly "stupid" ideas can be the catalyst for great ones. The more brainstorming and creative ideas you generate, the greater likelihood that the "right" name will pop out! Don't censor your ideas – the more the better. You can narrow down to your favorites later, when you'll do some research, and then choose the winner.

Initial Brainstorming

When answering the following questions, write down as many words (adjectives, nouns, verbs, adverbs) as possible. The first objective is a quantity of words, to get your creative juices flowing. Free associate and write down any related words. Keep your dictionary, thesaurus, and crossword dictionary handy to help you find synonyms and related words. After you have all your ideas on paper, go back and pick out your favorite ideas.

1. What are some words (adjectives, nouns, verbs) that describe the benefits of your coaching?

2. What benefits do you want your clients to get from your coaching?

3. What words describe who you are, how you are in the world, how you are as a coach, how you treat clients, or how you approach your work?

4. What image or feeling do you want to project with your business name?

5. What perceptions, images, or feelings do you want your potential clients to have when they read your business name?

6. What coaching-related words or terms do you like?

7. What words have special meaning to you?

8. What are names of local or regional streets, cities, counties, landmarks, mountain ranges, lakes, or other features? What are words related to these place-names?

9. How might your surname be used in the business name?

10. What foreign language words, or combinations of foreign language words, convey the image or feeling that you want to project?

11. What created names have meaning to you? Created names are parts of words, made-up words, or combinations of words that have meaning to you.

12. What legal element should be included in your name?

Notes:

Narrow Down the Options

13. Look over your brainstormed lists. What names are your top eight choices?

Potential Name	Pros	Cons

14. From the list above, which names do you want to further consider and research?

Researching the Names

15. Research your potential business names through the following resources:

❑   The Fictitious Business Name files in your County Clerk or Recorder's office

❑   Directories: local region, business, trade, coach referral services

❑   Trademark and Service Mark registry: www.uspto.gov

❑   Domain name registrations: www.networksolutions.com and www.register.com

❑   Search through the Internet, using several different search engines

❑   Search the Yellow Pages (both print and Internet)

And The Winner Is ....

1
Additional Resources

Standard Resources

- Dictionaries: standard, crossword, and foreign language

- Plumb Design Visual Thesaurus: www.plumbdesign.com/thesaurus/ (This is a cool tool to play with!)

- Research It!: www.itools.com/research-it/ (Has a dictionary, thesaurus, and translator)

- Roget's Thesaurus of Synonyms & Antonyms: www.thesaurus.com

Creativity Books

- Ayan, Jordan. *Aha!: 10 Ways to Free Your Creative Thinking and Find Your Great Ideas*. Crown Publishers, 1997.

- De Bono, Edward. *Lateral Thinking: Creativity Step-By-Step*. HarperCollins, 1990.

- Von Oech, Roger. *A Whack on the Side of the Head*. Warner Books, 1998.

- Von Oech, Roger. *Creative Whack Pack*. United States Games Systems, 1990.

- Von Oech, Roger. *A Kick in the Seat of the Pants*. HarperCollins, 1986.

- Wujec, Tom. *Five Star Mind: Games and Exercises to Stimulate Your Creativity and Imagination*. Main Street Books, 1995.

Sources to Research Existing Business Names

- Records of Fictitious Business Name petitions at your County Clerk or Recorder's Office

- Directories for local businesses may be available through your local Chamber of Commerce: http://clickcity.com/index2.htm

- U.S. and statewide business directories are expensive to purchase, as they are typically used for the development of sales leads. Check your local library for a copy. One vendor is: Directories USA: www.directoriesUSA.com

- Yellow Pages listings

    - Check your local library for copies of nearby telephone books

    - http://yellowpages.msn.com/Yellowpages

    - www.infobel.com/USA

Domain Name Research

- www.networksolutions.com. There is also a page called "Name Fetcher" that will help you construct and search related domain names.

- www.register.com. This site has a "Domain Fast Find" function that can help you develop a good domain name.

Well-known Search Engines:

- www.altavista.com

- www.aj.com (Ask Jeeves)

- www.google.com

- www.infoseek.com

- www.lycos.com

- www.excite.com

- www.yahoo.com

Trademark and Service Mark Research and Filing

- 4Trademark.com: www.trademark-search.com

- U.S. Patent and Trademark Office (USPTO): www.uspto.gov, (800) 786-9199 or (703) 308-HELP (4357). The USPTO web site allows free searching of existing trademarks and service marks through the TESS function.

- www.1-2-3-trademark.com

- www.trademark.com

Organization Directories

- Reference books at your library:

    - *National Trade and Professional Associations of the United States.* Columbia Books, 2000.

    - *Encyclopedia of Associations.* Gale Research, 2000.

2
Which Business Structure?

1. What business structure features are most important to you? Use the checklist below and the structure comparison table on the following page to determine which business structure is most appropriate for your current situation.

   ❑ I will be the sole owner.
   - Sole Proprietor
   - LLC (in most states)
   - S-Corporation (in most states)

   ❑ I will have another person as a partner in my business.
   - Partnership
   - LLC
   - S-Corporation

   ❑ I want to protect myself (and my family) from any personal liability for the business.
   - LLC
   - S-Corporation

   ❑ I want to use my state-licensed profession (such as therapist, CPA, lawyer, educator, nurse) within my coaching practice.
   - Sole Proprietor
   - Partnership
   - S-Corporation

   ❑ I don't want to do any additional paperwork to establish the company.
   - Sole Proprietor

   ❑ I don't want to pay any additional annual fees to the state.
   - Sole Proprietor
   - Partnership

Business Structure Comparison Table

Feature	Sole Proprietor	Partnership	LLC	S-Corp
Net income is not taxed at the business level	✔	✔	✔	✔
Structure can be used by businesses with only one owner (varies by state)	✔		✔	✔
Business is a legal entity separate from the owner		✔	✔	✔
Owner is personally liable for the business	✔	✔		
Owner has limited personal liability			✔	✔
Need to file forms with the Secretary of State to establish the business			✔	✔
Additional annual state tax or fee (varies by state)			✔	✔
File taxes with personal tax form	✔		✔ (one person LLC)	
Uses separate federal tax forms for the business filing		✔ (1065)	✔ (1065)	✔ (1120S)
State licensed professionals allowed	✔	✔		✔
EIN required	In some cases	✔	✔	✔
Separate financial accounts needed		✔	✔	✔
Need to document roles of each member		✔	✔	✔
Annual meeting required of members and owners with documented minutes			✔	✔

Note: Appendix C contains copies of frequently used IRS business-related tax forms.

2. List your top two choices and the trade-offs involved with each.

3. What additional action steps will you take to determine the best legal structure for your business?

   ❑ Talk with a lawyer knowledgeable about small-business legal structures

   ❑ Talk with an accountant knowledgeable about the financial implications of small-business legal structures

   ❑ Other:

4. The legal structure you have chosen to use for your business at this time is:

   ❑ Sole Proprietorship

   ❑ Partnership

   ❑ Limited Liability Company

   ❑ S-Corporation

5. What forms will you need to obtain and file to establish your company?

   • Sole Proprietor: None

   • Partnership:

      ❑ Partnership Agreement (between you and the other partners; keep in your files)

      ❑ Employee Identification Number (discussed in Chapter Three)

- LLC:
  - ❑ Articles of Organization (filed with the Secretary of State)
  - ❑ Operating Agreement (between you and the other members of the business; keep in your files)
  - ❑ Annual meeting minutes (keep in your files)
  - ❑ Employee Identification Number (discussed in Chapter Three)

- S-Corporation
  - ❑ Articles of Incorporation (filed with the Secretary of State)
  - ❑ IRS form 2533 – Election by a Small Business Corporation
  - ❑ Operating Agreement (between you and the other stockholders)
  - ❑ Annual meeting minutes (keep in your files)
  - ❑ Annual forms to continue pass-through tax treatment
  - ❑ Employee Identification Number (discussed in Chapter Three)

6. If you choose to use the Partnership, LLC, or S-Corporation structures, will you:

   ❑ Complete and file the business establishment paperwork yourself?

   ❑ Hire another company or lawyer to complete and file the paperwork?

2
Additional Resources

The IRS

Note: Appendix C contains copies of frequently used federal tax forms associated with each business structure.

The IRS has a well-organized and informative web site (www.irs.gov), including an extensive section for small businesses. Specific publications related to business structures include:

- Pub #334: Tax Guide for Small Businesses (geared towards sole proprietors)

- Pub #541: Partnerships (Note: The IRS does not have a specific publication for LLCs, because they are treated like partnerships from a tax perspective.)

- Pub #542: Corporations

Phone numbers for the IRS include:

- Live telephone assistance: (800) 829-1040

- To order forms or publications via fax-on-demand: (703) 368-9694

- To order forms or publications by phone: (800) Tax-Form (800-829-3676)

Books

- Nolo Press (www.nolo.com) has hundreds of comprehensive small-business legal books and a very informative web site. (800) 992-6656.

- Clifford, Denis and Ralph Warner. *The Partnership Book – How to Write a Partnership Agreement.* Nolo Press, 1997.

- Dicks, J.W. *Form Your Own Corporation and Launch a Business In Any State.* Adams Media Corporation, 2000.

- Mancuso, Anthony. *Form Your Own Limited Liability Company.* Nolo Press, 2000.

- Mancuso, Anthony. *Nolo's Quick LLC – All You Need to Know About Limited Liability Companies.* Nolo Press, 2000.

- Minars, David. *Corporations Step By Step*. Barrons Legal-Ease, 1996.

- Minars, David. *Partnerships Step By Step*. Barrons Legal-Ease, 1997.

- Sitarz, Daniel. *Incorporate Your Business – The National Corporation Kit*. Nova Publishing Company, 1997.

- Sitarz, Daniel. *Small Business Start Up Kit – S Corporations*. Nova Publishing Company, 2000.

Incorporation and LLC Filing Web Sites

There are many sites that will do the filings for you (LLC, S-Corporation), walk you through the process, or sell you a kit to do it yourself. All for a fee, of course. You may be able to get the same forms and some level of instructions from your Secretary of State, but those may not be quite as user friendly.

- www.123-newcorp.com

- www.4inc.com

- www.accessincorp.com

- www.corpamerica.com

- www.corporate.com

- www.inc123.com

- www.incorporatetime.com

- www.mycorporation.com

- www.start-a-business.com

Online Ready-made LLC Forms

For a small fee, you can download ready-made LLC forms (Articles of Organization and Operating Agreements). To complete the forms, you only need to supply your unique information (for example, name, address, allotment of net income to owners). Some of these forms have been tailored to suit specific situations, such as a husband and wife LLC.

- Alberty Publishing LLC: www.alberty.com.

3
More Government Hoops

Fictitious Business Name

1. Does your business name include all the owners' surnames? If not, you will need to file a Petition for a Fictitious Business Name with your County Clerk or Recorder. An FBN petition must be filed within 40 days of starting your business.

    •   The County Clerk/Recorder's phone number is:

    •   The County Clerk/Recorder's office address and hours are:

    •   Describe your local FBN process:

        •   What is the cost to file the petition at the County Clerk/Recorder's office?

        •   How many days does the notice need to run in the paper?

        •   Use the table below to list which newspapers are acceptable for the FBN process, and to compare listing costs.

Newspaper Name	Phone Number	Cost

Employer Identification Number

2. You should apply for an EIN for your company if you answer Yes to any of the following questions:

   ❑ Is your business an LLC with more than one owner? Note: you can apply for an EIN if you are a one-person LLC, but it is not required.

   ❑ Is your business an S-Corporation?

   ❑ Is your business a Partnership?

   ❑ Does/will your business have any employees?

   ❑ Do you/will you have a Keogh retirement savings plan (discussed in Chapter Eight)?

   If your company needs an EIN, you will file IRS form SS-4, which can be downloaded from the IRS web site (www.irs.gov) or by calling (800) TAX-FORM.

   Record your EIN number here:

   Date you received your EIN:

   Notes:

Licensing and Permits

3. List what cities you plan to practice in. Note the phone number for each City Licensing Department. Call to find out if you will need a business license to work within that city, referring either to the physical location of your office or the locations of your clients.

City Name	City Licensing Dept Phone Number	Is a Business License needed?

4. Call your County and/or City Planning and Clerks offices to determine if any additional licenses or permits are needed for your business.

5. If you will be selling any products, such as books, workbooks, audio tapes, or other materials, you will need a sales tax license or seller's permit or resale license (the wording varies across states). Call your State Treasury office or Board of Equalization to find out how to apply for this license and/or permit.

Record your license or permit number here:

Zoning Requirements

6. Contact the following offices to learn about any zoning restrictions related to home-based businesses in your neighborhood.

   - County Planning department

   - City Planning department

7. What private land use restrictions are in effect for your neighborhood? You might find these restrictions in any of the following documents:

   - Property deeds (restrictive covenants)

   - Subdivision covenants, conditions, and restrictions (CC&Rs)

   - Planned unit development (PUD) rules

   - Condo regulations

   - Co-op regulations

   - Leases or rental agreements

8. Contact the following organizations for additional information on local permit, licensing, or zoning requirements:

☐ Your local Small Business Development Center (www.sba.gov/sbdc/)

☐ The Small Business Division of your state's Department of Commerce

☐ Your local Service Corps of Retired Executives (SCORE): www.score.org

3
Additional Resources

Internal Revenue Service (IRS)

The IRS has an informative, clearly organized, and well-written web site at www.irs.gov. The "Tax Information for Business" section covers a wide range of tax-related subjects. One publication is related to this chapter:

- Publication # 1635, Understanding Your EIN.

Other Government Resources

- The Small Business Division of your state's Department of Commerce is a good source for information concerning any state license or permit requirements.

- Your nearest Small Business Development Center (SBDC) may have additional information on local requirements. The SBDCs are a resource partner of the Federal Small Business Administration office. www.sba.gov/sbdc/

- The Service Corps of Retired Executives (SCORE) is a nonprofit organization dedicated to the success of small businesses, and typically works closely with the SBDCs. www.score.org.

4
Business Contact Information

Street Address

1. Research and select the best option for your mailing address:

   ❑ Your home address

   ❑ U.S. Post Office box

   ❑ Mail receiving service center (e.g. Mail Boxes Etc., Postal Express)

   ❑ Office space that you rent or lease

   ❑ Serviced office

Company Name: Features and Services			
Startup cost			
Monthly cost			
Length of contract			
Other services provided			
Convenience of location			
Days and hours of access			
Notes			

Business Phone and Fax Number

2. Which business phone and fax alternatives do you want to use?

    ❑ Voicemail

    ❑ Answering machine

    ❑ Separate business number

    ❑ Toll-free number

    ❑ Separate fax number

    ❑ Telephone Line Sharing Device for routing calls to fax machine

    ❑ Internet-based fax receiving service

    ❑ Mobile phone

3. Research the costs associated with a separate business telephone or fax line.

Type of Phone Line: Features and Services	Standard Phone Line	ISDN Line	DSL Line
Installation costs - Labor			
Installation costs - Equipment			
Monthly base charge			
Per minute charge for local calls: day / evening			
Per minute charge for local toll calls: day / evening			
Hours for day and evening rates			
Monthly charge for voicemail			
Notes			

4. Compare long distance telephone services.

Company Name: Features and Services			
Monthly base charge			
Local toll call rate (per minute)			
Hours for day and evening rates			
Intrastate rate (within your state) day/night			
Interstate rate (state to state) day/night			
Billing increments (number of seconds)			
Calling card rate day/night			
Cost for set-up of toll-free number			
Monthly base charge for toll-free number			
Cost of toll free calls day/night			
Is a direct toll free number assigned, or is the caller required to enter an ID number? (PIN)			

Notes:

5. Compare mobile phone services.

Company Name: **Features and Services**			
Startup costs			
Monthly base charge			
Number of peak minutes included			
Number of non-peak and/or weekend minutes included			
Peak per minute charge			
Non-peak per minute charge			
Billing increments (number of seconds)			
Geographic coverage area			
Contract length			
Per minute roaming charge			
Monthly charge for voicemail			

Notes:

Internet Access and Use

6. Compare Internet Service Providers.

   Tip: Before you gather information on an ISP's remote access capabilities, write down the cities (and zip codes if you know them) where you routinely travel.

Company Name: **Features and Services**			
Local access number			

Remote access numbers
    City/Location:
 	
    City/Location:
 	
    City/Location:
 	
    City/Location:			

Monthly base charge			
Any additional charges?			
Connection methods supported (e.g., modem, ISDN, DSL, cable, satellite)			
Dial-up or full-time connection?			
Customer service days and hours. Is it a toll-free number?			
What email services are provided?			
What amount of web site space do they provide?			

Internet Access Methods Comparison Table

Feature	Analog Modem	ISDN	Cable	DSL	Satellite
Method is portable	✓				
ISP acceptance	All	Most	Some	Some	Only two companies. All ISPs for modem upload.
Type of line used	Regular phone	Special phone	Cable	Regular phone	Satellite and regular phone
Speed (download/upload)	56K* / 30K	112K –128K upload/download (two channel)	10x ISDN ** Upload ranges 10x ISDN to 30K	6x ISDN / 3x ISDN	3x ISDN / 30K
Dial-up mode available	✓	✓	✓ depends on company		✓
Full-time hookup	Available	Available	✓ depends on company	✓	Available
Monthly cost	Flat fee, approx. $20	Flat fee or usage based, approx. $70–100	Flat fee, approx. $30–60	Flat fee, approx. $30–60	Flat fee, approx. $30–60
Start-up costs	Approx. $100	Approx. $300	Approx. $300	Approx. $300	Approx. $400
Availability of service	Everywhere w/phone	Less available	Less available	Less available	Everywhere w/phone and clear south-facing view
Can share line with fax/voice and Internet access		✓		✓	

NOTES

All figures listed are approximate and current as of the date of publication. Actual performance may vary based on location and specific requirements.

* 56K is the maximum theoretical download speed for analog modems. However, 53K is the maximum actual download speed. Typical actual speeds may range from 40–48K.

** With cable access to the Internet, download speed can vary substantially based on the number of other simultaneous users in the neighborhood. The number listed here is the theoretical speed. The other access methods typically do not have wide variation in download speed. Upload speed is dependent on the access method used—cable or analog modem.

7. Write your notes here from your research on the various Internet connection alternatives:

❑ Analog modem

❑ ISDN

❑ Cable

❑ DSL

❑ Satellite

8. Compare the features of Email Service Providers

   • Number of email boxes needed:

Company Name: Features and Services			
Monthly base charge			
Any additional charges?			
Number of boxes provided			
Customer service days and hours. Is it a toll-free number?			
Web-based email access supported?			
Email software required			
Other features/services provided			

9. Domain Name

   • Desired domain name:

   • Research the availability of the domain name at either www.networksolutions.com or www.register.com

   • Will you use the domain name now, or park it?

10. Compare web hosting service providers

Company Name: Features and Services			
Monthly base charge			
Any additional charges?			
Length of contract			
Customer service days and hours. Is it a toll-free number?			
Amount of disk space provided			
Number of email boxes provided			
Web based email			
Transfer limit			
Hit counter			
Web based administrative tools *			
Are FrontPage 2000 Extensions supported?			
Access to web site activity logs			

* Web based administrative tools allow the web site owner (you) to perform some basic tasks without having to call customer service. These tasks might include adding and deleting users and email accounts, changing email passwords, updating user information, posting a vacation message, setting up email forwarding, and performing basic web site security tasks.

4
Additional Resources

Street Address

- US Postal Service: http://new.usps.com

- A searchable database of over 9000 mailbox rental and packaging stores can be found at: www.bnl.com/mb.

Long Distance Carrier

- An inexpensive long distance carrier offering low cost toll-free numbers is: America's Co-op/ NTA: (800) 600-5553. At time of printing, America's Co-op had been purchased by National Telecom Association and was in the process of merging with PowerNet Global Communications. A brief informational web site is at http://achieveusa.freeyellow.com/ or www.ntanet.com. This service can be used for long-distance, toll, and toll-free services.

Telephone Line Sharing Devices

- Your local office supply store

- Computer Peripheral Systems Inc.: www.cpscom.com

- LSDI (Line Share Devices, Inc.): www.lineshare.com

Receiving Faxes and Voicemail through Email

- www.efax.com

- www.jfax.com

Internet-based PC-to-phone and PC-to-PC services

- FreeIP.com: www.freenetcalls.com/free-internet-phonecalls.html

- Net2Phone: www.net2phone.com

- PhoneFree: www.phonefree.com

Internet Service Providers (ISPs)

- The List: The definitive ISP Buyer's Guide, offered by www.internet.com

- www.ispcheck.com - Can search for local ISPs and web hosts

Trying to make sense of the various technical terms?

Check out these three sources for more information and tutorials on terms and concepts like modem, ISDN, DSL, ISP, and web hosting.

- http://netforbeginners.about.com

- www.learnthenet.com

- www.whatis.com

Travel Items to Use with an Analog Modem

- Digital Phone Line Tester, Cross Over Adaptor, Polarity Reverser, and Deluxe Patch Cord Kit available through Magellan's Travel Supply catalog (800) 962-4943, or www.magellans.com

Satellite Internet Connection

- DirecPC: www.direcpc.com

- StarBand Communications: www.starband.com

Domain Name Research and Registration

- www.networksolutions.com

- www.register.com

Web Hosting Information and Ranking

- www.hostindex.com

- www.hostsearch.com

- www.ispcheck.com

- www.tophosts.com

- www.webhostlist.com

Financial Matters

To fulfill a dream, …..
to be given the chance to create, is the meat and potatoes of life.
The money is the gravy. As everyone else, I love to dunk my crust in it.
But alone, it is not a diet designed to keep body and soul together.

BETTE DAVIS

5: Money Management
- Record Keeping
- Budgeting
- Financial Accounts
- Accounts Payable
- Invoicing
- Payments

6: Insurance
- What Insurance Do You Need?
- Finding the Right Insurance Agent
- Key Insurance Terms
- Business Property Insurance
- Automobile Insurance
- Business Liability Insurance
- Business Interruption Insurance
- Bundled Insurance Plans
- Health Insurance
- Disability Insurance
- Errors and Omissions Insurance

7: Business Taxes
- Business Deductions
- Estimated Tax Payments
- 1099 Forms
- Annual Filing
- Self-Employment Tax

8: Retirement Plans
- SEP-IRA
- KEOGH Plans

5
Money Management

Record Keeping

1. How will you manage your business financial records?

    ❑ Financial management
       software program
         • Which program?

    ❑ With a PC spreadsheet

    ❑ Bookkeeper or accountant

    ❑ With pencil and paper

2. What process will you use to keep track of your billable time?

A suggested format for a billable time worksheet is:

Coaching Sessions and Billing Log
Client: Jane Smith

Month	Session Dates	$ Amt	Billed Date	Date Rcvd
January 2001	9, 16, 23, 30	$200	12/18/00	1/5 chk #2396
February	5, 12, 19, 26	$200	1/22/01	2/1 chk #2428
March	2, 9, 16, 23	$200	2/16	3/5 chk #2450
April	6,13,20	$150	3/23	4/2 chk #2463
May	2, 16, 23, 30	$200	4/23	5/4 chk #2489

3. What process will you use to create and organize your paper trail?
    • Where will you keep your receipts?
    • How will you track them?

Business Expenses

4. Following is a list of typical business expense categories. Which ones will be applicable for your business?

☐ Accounting/bookkeeping, and financial consulting fees
☐ Advertising expenses
☐ Automobile expenses (only the percent that is used for business)
☐ Bank service charges and fees
☐ Books and periodicals
☐ Business/trade conventions
☐ Business gifts (annual limit of $25 per recipient)
☐ Business meals (50% is deductible)
☐ Coaching fees, if related to your business
☐ Computer, printer, and software (if used over 50% for the business)
☐ Consultant fees
☐ Depreciation and amortization
☐ Dues for professional and trade associations
☐ Education expenses for maintaining or improving required skills
☐ Email, Internet access, and web hosting services
☐ Fax machine
☐ Insurance expense
☐ Legal and attorney fees
☐ License fees and taxes
☐ Merchant account or credit card processing fees
☐ Office furniture and equipment
☐ Office supplies
☐ Online services used for the business
☐ Parking and tolls
☐ Postage and shipping
☐ Printing and duplication
☐ Self-employment taxes
☐ Start-up expenses (amortized over 60 months)
☐ State and local business taxes
☐ Preparation of business tax return
☐ Telephone expense (only for a separate business line)
☐ Travel expenses

Budgeting

5. Below is an example budget for a start-up coaching practice. Create your own
    budget using the blank template on the following page.

Budget for My Coaching Practice
For January – March, 2001

	Jan	Feb	Mar	Qtr. Total	Notes
Income					
Coaching	0	400	1000	1,400	
Start-up Costs					
Duplication expense	10			10	coaching flyers
Travel expenses	150			150	travel to training
Office supplies	35			35	
Professional development	50			50	coach training
Business Expenses					
Advertising			50	50	ad in newsletter
Bank charges		5	5	10	
Books and resources		40	25	65	
Business insurance					
Business meals		25	25	50	
Duplication expense		10	10	20	flyers, brochures
Internet access		20	20	40	
Legal fees			150	150	LLC filing
Marketing expenses		50		50	biz cards
Miscellaneous		25	25	50	
Office equipment		100		100	new chair
Office rent					
Office supplies		20	35	55	
Parking and tolls		5	10	15	
Postage and shipping		10	10	20	
Professional development		150		150	coach training
Professional dues			50	50	ICF chapter
Telephone		25	25	50	
Travel expenses		45	45	90	
Total Expenses	**245**	**530**	**485**	**1,260**	
Net profit (loss)	(245)	(130)	515	140	
Taxes @ 20% per quarter				28	
After tax profit (loss)	**(245)**	**(130)**	**515**	**112**	
Cumulative profit (loss)	(245)	(375)	140		

Budget for:

For time period of:

Month:				Qtr. Total	Notes
Income					
Start-up Costs^					
Business Expenses					
Total Expenses					
* Net profit (loss)					
Taxes @ 20% per qtr.					
**** After tax profit (loss)**					
Cumulative profit (loss)					

Note: * Net profit (loss) is income less total expenses. ** After tax profit (loss) is net profit minus taxes. There is no tax on a loss. *** Cumulative profit (loss) is the sum of previous month's cumulative profit (loss) plus current month's after tax profit. ^ Startup costs are amortized over 60 months.

Financial Accounts and Accounts Payable

6. List your business checking account information

   Bank name and address:

   Account Number:

7. List your business credit card information

8. How will you pay your business bills?

   ❑ By hand

   ❑ With financial management
   software

   ❑ With an online bill payment
   service

   ❑ Online direct to the company

   ❑ Automatic deduction from my
   bank account

9. Compare online bill payment services

Company Name: Features and Services			
Monthly base charge			
Per transaction charge			
Downloads to your Financial Mgmt Program			
Expense reports provided			
Email notice when bills arrive			
Can set up select bills for automatically recurring payments			
Can do bill review and payment by phone			

Invoicing

10. How will you create your invoices?

❑ With my financial management software

❑ Word processing program

❑ Spreadsheet program

❑ With an email based billing system (e.g., PayPal)

❑ Preprinted invoice form

Below is an example invoice.

My Coaching Practice
1234 Elm Street
Any Town, CA 00000

Invoice
April 20, 2001
Invoice # 126

Bill To: Carolyn Client
984 Maple Street
Another Town, CA 00000

Description

Personal Coaching Services, May 1 – 31 2001
2 hours @ $100.00

Total Due: $200.00

Payment Due Date: May 8, 2001

It's a pleasure working with you!
Please remit payment to address above.

EIN # 99-99999999

---

11. What forms of payment will you accept?

❑ Check

❑ Credit card

❑ Electronic Funds Transfer

❑ Cash

❑ Barter

12. Use the table below to compare Merchant Bank services

Company Name: Features and Services			
Start-up fees			
Monthly minimum charge			
Discount Fee – MasterCard & Visa			
Discount Fee – American Express			
Additional transaction fees			
Gateway fee			
Other monthly fees			
Reporting fee			
Other services			

Notes:

5
Additional Resources

Books on Financial Planning

- Orman, Suze. *The Nine Steps to Financial Freedom*. Crown Publishers, 1997.

- Orman, Suze. *You've Earned It, Don't Lose It*. Newmarket Press, 1997.

- Orman, Suze. *The Courage to be Rich: Creating a Life of Material and Spiritual Abundance*. Riverhead Books, 1999.

Financial Management Software

- Intuit: www.intuit.com

- Microsoft: http://www.microsoft.com/insider/finance.htm

- MYOB: www.myob.com

- Peachtree: www.peachtree.com

Time Tracking and Expense Software

- Free version of Timesheet on the Internet: www.journeyx.com

- Journeyx Timesheet: www.journeyx.com

- PandaWare TimeCache 3.0 for the Mac: www.pandaware.com/timecache

- TimeSlice: www.mauisoftware.com

- www.timeslips.com

Internet Banking

- http://www.netbank.com

- http://www.wingspan.com

Financial Accounts and Accounts Payable

- Bank of America: www.bankofamerica.com

- Citibank Business Card through American Airlines: (800) 732-6000

- Quicken Business Card: (800) 638-1520

- Vanguard: www.vanguard.com

Business Checks and Supplies

- ASAP Checks, Forms, and Supplies: www.sensible-solutions.com

- Deluxe Business Checks and Forms: www.deluxeforms.com

- McBee: www.mcbeesystems.com

- NEBS: www.nebs.com

- www.ChecksUnlimited.com

Online Bill Payment Services

- Bankrate.com: http://www.bankrate.com/brm/publ/onlifees.asp – Has a table of costs to do online banking by institution

- Checkfree: www.checkfree.com

- www.Billpaynet.com

- www.PayMyBills.com

Online Payment Service Companies

- www.acteva.com

- www.billpoint.com

- www.ccnow.com

- www.PayPal.com

Merchant Credit Card Accounts

- Practice Pay Solutions, (800) 326-9897: www.practicepaysolutions.com

Internet Barter Sites

- www.barter.net

- www.bartertrust.com

- www.bigvine.com

- www.intellibarter.com

- www.ubarter.com

6
Insurance

1. Review your personal insurance policies to see what type of business coverage they include. Note the coverage limits and exclusions below.

   Homeowner's or Apartment Dweller's insurance (for business property and/or business liability coverage):

   Personal liability insurance (for business liability coverage):

   Automobile insurance (for coverage while you are conducting business):

   Health insurance (coverage for work related injury):

   Disability insurance:

2. What is the approximate value of the personal assets you want to protect? (for example, your home, car, savings, future earnings, retirement funds, property)

3. Is your income the sole support for your family? How long could you manage on just your savings or on your spouse's / significant other's income?

4. Based on your previous answers, what types of insurance do you need to further research? Listed below are options available for each type of insurance you might need.

    ❏ Business Property

    - Is your existing homeowner's policy sufficient?

    - Can you get an endorsement for your homeowner's policy?

    - Look into a bundled plan

    ❏ Automobile

    - Can you change the classification of your auto usage to "business/personal"?

    - Do you need a separate business auto policy?

    ❏ Business Liability

    - Do you want a stand-alone business liability policy?

    - Look into a bundled plan

❑ Business Interruption

- Basic plan only

- Do you want extra expense coverage?

❑ Bundled Plans (business property, liability, business interruption)

- In-home policy

- Business owner's policy (typically has inventory coverage)

❑ Health Insurance

- Can you be added to your spouse's insurance?

- Look into group policies

- Look into individual policies

❑ Disability Insurance

❑ Errors and Omissions

5. How often do you back up your business-related data (e.g., monthly, quarterly)?

6. At what off-site location will you store the back-up data (e.g., safe deposit box, friend's or relative's house)?

7. Do you have a record of your business property, including a description, date of purchase, and purchase price? Below is a list of typical business equipment.

Item	Description (e.g. brand, size, model number)	Purchase Date	Purchase Price
Telephone equipment			
Desktop computer			
Portable computer			
Computer software programs			
Computer monitor			
Printer			
Fax machine			
Scanner			
Books			
Other resource materials			
Office furniture: • Chair • Desk • Lamp • Shelves • Table • File cabinet			
PDA (e.g. Palm Pilot)			
Mobile phone			

8. Insurance policy comparison worksheet

Use this worksheet to document and compare the various insurance policies that you research.

Company Name: Features and Services			
Type of Insurance			
Phone number / contact name			
Source of information (e.g. web site, verbal, printed information)			
Premium (annual or monthly)			
Deductibles			
Coverage limits			
Exclusions			

6
Additional Resources

General Insurance References and Sources

- Association of Small Business Development Centers: www.asbdc-us.org

- Chamber of Commerce can be located through:

    - International Chamber of Commerce directory:
      http://clickcity.com/index2.htm

    - Or the yellow pages: http://yp.yahoo.com, or
      http://yellowpages.msn.com

- The Hartford Insurance Company: www.thehartford.com

- http://insurance.yahoo.com

- Insurance Information Institute: www.iii.org

- International Coach Federation: www.coachfederation.org has several
  insurance offerings for ICF members:

    - Loomis Insurance Agency (716) 385-2900. An insurance program
      designed especially for the members of ICF, providing an affordable
      package of business property, computer, and liability insurance,
      including professional insurance for members

    - Theresa A. Goldstein (716) 385-2900, offering a package with business
      property, computer, and liability insurance.

    - National Association of Socially Responsible Organizations – health
      insurance coverage, including dental: www.nasro-co-op.com or (800)
      638-8113

- National Association for the Self-Employed: www.nase.org

- National Federation of Independent Business is for smaller employers (fewer
  than 25 employees): (202) 554-9000

- Small Business Benefit Association: www.sbba.com – group health policies

- State Farm Insurance: www.statefarm.com

- www.4insurance.com

- www.allbusiness.com

- www.bizbuyer.com – Includes business insurance buying guides, links to states' insurance departments, focus mostly on health insurance

- www.insuremarket.com

- www.quotesmith.com

- www.safeware.com or (800) 848-3469, for coverage of computers, PDAs, laptops, both in the office and when travelling

- www.smallbusinesscenter.com

7
Business Taxes

1. Which federal income tax form is used for your business structure?

   ❑ 1040 Schedule C or C-EZ (for sole proprietors and one-person LLCs)

   ❑ 1065 and K-1s (for partnerships and LLCs)

   ❑ 1120-S and K-1s (for S-Corporations)

   Appendix C includes copies of the most widely used federal business tax forms.

2. Call your state tax department to determine which specific state tax forms are needed for your business.

3. From Chapter Five, review the list of typical business expenses and the budget you created. Based on what you have learned about tax deductions, are there any additional expense or budget line items to add to your budget and financial plans?

4. What start-up expenses (expenses prior to receiving any income) have you incurred? These expenses are to be amortized over the first 60 months of your business.

5. Are you eligible for the home office deduction? The criteria are:

   - The part of your home you wish to claim as a business expense must be used *exclusively* and *regularly* for business and one of the following:

      ❏ Your principal place of business, or

      ❏ A place where you meet with customers or clients in the normal course of business, or

      ❏ In connection with your business, if you use a separate structure that is not attached to your home, or

      ❏ For the administrative or management activities of your business and you have no other fixed location where you conduct substantial administrative or management activities of your business.

6. How will you handle your estimated tax payments?

   ❏ Just wait for my annual tax payment and pay the underpayment penalty

   ❏ Pay last year's tax amount, and then any additional amount due with my annual tax return

   ❏ Estimate and pay the taxes quarter by quarter

7. How will you prepare your annual tax return?

   ❏ With my own tax software

   ❏ Hiring a professional tax preparer

   ❏ By hand

8. Will you need to issue any 1099s? Example service providers that might require a 1099 include: attorney, CPA, graphic designer, coach, office assistant, computer consultant, business consultant, or bookkeeper.

   - If you need to send out 1099s,

     ❑ Order the 1099 and 1096 forms from the IRS (1-800-tax-form)

     ❑ Make a list of the 1099 recipients:

       •

       •

       •

       •

   - Do you need to receive 1099s from any of your clients? If yes, from whom?

9. Review the list of IRS forms and publications in the Additional Resources section. Which ones will you need? Make sure to call the IRS (1-800-tax-form) early in the year before the tax season rush. You can also order (or download) forms and publications from the web site at www.irs.gov.

7
Additional Resources

The Internal Revenue Service

The IRS offers many free publications of interest to individuals and businesses, as well as an informative web site (www.irs.gov). Phone numbers for the IRS include:

- Live telephone assistance: (800) 829-1040

- To order forms or publications via fax-on-demand: (703) 368-9694

- To order forms or publications by phone: (800) Tax-Form (829-3676)

Listed below are IRS publications relating to small businesses. These can all be downloaded from the IRS web site, or you can call to order them or use their fax-on-demand service.

- #334: Tax Guide for Small Business

- #463: Travel, Entertainment, Gift, and Car Expenses

- #505: Tax Withholding and Estimated Tax

- #508: Tax Benefits for Work Related Education

- #509: Tax Calendars for Year 2001

- #525: Taxable and Non-Taxable Income

- #529: Miscellaneous Deductions

- #533: Self-Employment Tax

- #535: Business Expenses

- #538: Accounting Periods and Methods

- #541: Partnerships (information is also applicable to LLCs)

- #542: Corporations (includes S-Corporations)

- #551: Basis of Assets

- #552: Recordkeeping for Individuals

- #553: Highlights of Tax Changes

- #560: Retirement Plans for Small Business

- #583: Starting a Business and Keeping Records

- #587: Business Use of Your Home

- #910: Guide to Free Tax Services

- #946: How to Depreciate Property

- #969: Medical Savings Accounts

- #1066: Small Business Tax Workshop Workbook

- #1635: Understanding Your EIN

- #1853: Small Business Talk

Sources for Tax Forms (1099s and 1096s)

- Deluxe Business Checks and Forms: www.deluxeforms.com

- IRS: www.irs.gov

- McBee: www.mcbeesystems.com

- NEBS: www.nebs.com

Tax Information and Preparation Books

- Carter, Gary W. *J. K. Lasser's Taxes Made Easy for Your Home-Based Business*. MacMillan General Reference, 2000.

- Fellman, Henry Aiy'm. *Keep Your Hard-Earned Money: Tax-Saving Solutions for the Self-Employed*. Pocket Books, 1998.

- Fleury, Robert E. *The Small Business Survival Guide: How to Manage Your Cash, Profits and Taxes*. Sourcebooks Trade, 1995.

- Lickson, Charles P. *Finance and Taxes for the Home-Based Business*. Crisp Publications, 1997.

- Ray, Norm. *Smart Tax Write-Offs: Hundreds of Tax Deduction Ideas for Home-Based Businesses, Independent Contractors, All Entrepreneurs.* Rayve Productions, 2000.

- Zobel, Jan. *Minding Her Own Business: The Self-Employed Woman's Guide to Taxes and Recordkeeping.* Adams Media Corporation, 2000.

Online Tax Resources

- H & R Block: www.hrblock/tax_center

- IRS: www.irs.gov

- MoneyCentral: moneycentral.msn.com/tax/home.asp

- Quicken: www.quicken.com/taxes

- Yahoo! Tax Center: taxes.yahoo.com

8
Retirement plans

1. Have you developed a financial plan for your retirement savings? If not, a recommended online, self-paced workshop is available through MoneyCentral at http://moneycentral.msn.com/retire/workshop/welcome.asp

   Document what you learn from this workshop:

2. Do you have a 401(k) or similar type of retirement account with your current employer? If yes, there are basically three alternatives to choose from when you leave that employer:

   - Leave the funds in the account (if allowed by the plan)

   - Take a distribution of the funds (and pay the early withdrawal penalties)

   - Move the funds into a Rollover IRA (available through any one of the companies listed in the Additional Resources section)

3. What type of retirement account do you want to set up for your business?

☐ SEP-IRA

☐ KEOGH, with one of the following structures:

- Money Purchase alone
  constant % of net income to invest: _____
  (max of 25%)

- Profit Sharing alone
  initial % of net income to invest: _____
  (max of 15%, but you can vary this amount each year)

- Paired Plan
  Money Purchase fixed at 10% a year
  Profit Sharing initial % of net income to invest: _____ (max of 15%)

4. Do you want to actively manage your retirement account (e.g., select what to invest in, when, and how much)? If yes, then you will want to look into *discount brokerages*. The largest ones are currently Fidelity, Vanguard, and Charles Schwab. If no, then you will want a full-service brokerage, which will provide a professional money manager to oversee your account and determine where to invest, when, and how much. The largest of these are currently Merrill Lynch and Prudential. The full-serviced, or managed, accounts have higher fees so the return on your investment will be lower. Use the table below to compare services.

Company Name: Features and Services			
Is it a full service brokerage or discount brokerage?			
Annual fees			
Other charges (e.g., commissions)			
Ease of access (internet, 24 hour support, toll-free number)			
Wide variety of investment choices			

8
Additional Resources

Books about Financial Planning

- Orman, Suze. *The Nine Steps to Financial Freedom*. Crown Publishers, 1997.

- Orman, Suze. *You've Earned It, Don't Lose It*. Newmarket Press, 1997.

- Orman, Suze. *The Courage to be Rich: Creating a Life of Material and Spiritual Abundance*. Riverhead Books, 1999.

General Retirement Planning Information

- IRS publication #560: Retirement Plans for Small Business

- Money Central's Step-by-Step Guide for Retirement Planning: http://moneycentral.msn.com/retire/home.asp

- Quicken.com information on retirement: www.quicken.com/retirement

- Quicken.com information on small business retirement plans: http://quicken.aol.com/retirement/small_business_IRAs/

Brokerages and Mutual Fund Companies

- Charles Schwab: www.charlesschwab.com

- Fidelity: www.fidelity.com (very informative site; also offers plans)

- Merrill Lynch: www.merrilllynch.com or www.askmerrill.com

- Prudential: www.prudential.com

- Vanguard: www.vanguard.com (very informative site; also offers plans)

Marketing and Communications

In the modern world of business, it is useless to be a creative original thinker unless you can also sell what you create. Management cannot be expected to recognize a good idea unless it is presented to them by a good salesman.

DAVID M. OGILVY

9: Your Marketing Plan
- Self Assessment
- Target Market Definition
- Short-term Business Goals
- Short-term Action Plan
- Marketing Activities

10: Marketing Materials
- Elevator Speech
- Business Card and Logo
- Brochures
- Introduction Letters
- Fliers and Information Sheets
- Business Web Site

11: Effective Networking
- Finding the Venues
- Event Preparation
- Attending Events
- After the Event

9
Your Marketing Plan

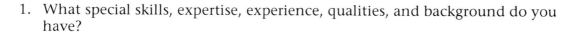

Self-Assessment

1. What special skills, expertise, experience, qualities, and background do you have?

2. Which of these special attributes do you want to highlight in your coaching practice and marketing activities?

3. Review your notes from Chapter One when you were naming your business. What additional qualities or personal attributes did you highlight during that process?

Target Market Definitions

4. List all the niches (i.e., groups of people) that you interact with or notice around you. Look at your everyday life: work, social groups, play groups, sports and recreation, church, volunteer activities.

5. Which of these niches interest you? Which ones will you focus on first and actively reach out to?

Name of Niche	How will you reach out to this niche?	Priority of Niche (H, M, L)

6. What niche are you interested in, but don't currently have access to?

7. What specific individuals will you reach out to within you current "sphere of influence" (your acquaintances)?

   What do you want to ask or tell them?

Name	Target deadline	Complete?

Short-term Business Goals

8. List your business goals for the next six months. Don't list the activities needed to reach the goal. Instead, just list the end goal. Which three to five of these goals are the highest priority?

Goal description	How will you measure your progress?	Priority (H, M, L)
Example: My practice has 15 paying clients.	Number of paying clients	High

Short-term Action Plan

9. Develop your marketing activity plan to support your goals. Use a check mark to denote the timing of the activity (i.e., month 1-2, 3-4, 5-6). Post your list in a visible place and share your plans with other people.

Month 1-2	Month 3-4	Month 5-6	Marketing Activity Description
✓	✓	✓	Example: Do 12 sample sessions a month
			1.
			2.
			3.
			4.
			5.
			6.
			7.
			8.
			9.
			10.
			11.
			12.

9
Additional Resources

Marketing Books

- Beckwith, Harry. *Selling the Invisible, A Field Guide to Modern Marketing.* Warner Books, 1997.

- Brodsky, Bart. *Finding Your Niche: Marketing Your Professional Service.* Community Resource Institute, 1991.

- Falkenstein, Lynda. *Nichecraft: Using Your Specialness to Focus Your Business, Corner Your Market and Make Customers Seek You Out.* Niche Press, 2000.

- Gordon, Kim T. *Bringing Home the Business: The 30 Truths Every Home Business Owner Must Know.* Perigee, 2000.

- Hayden, C.J. *Get Clients Now! A 28-Day Marketing Program for Professionals and Consultants.* Amacom, 1999.

- Hiam, Alexander. *Marketing for Dummies.* IDG Books Worldwide, 1997.

- Levinson, Jay and Seth Godin. *Get What You Deserve, How to Guerrilla Market Yourself.* Avon Books, 1997.

- Levinson, Jay. *Guerrilla Marketing Excellence: The Fifty Golden Rules for Small Business Success.* Houghton Mifflin Company, 1993.

- Levinson, Jay, and Seth Godin. *The Guerrilla Marketing Handbook.* Houghton Mifflin Company, 1994.

- Levinson, Jay. *Guerrilla Marketing: Secrets for Making Big Profits from Your Small Business.* Houghton Mifflin Company, 1998.

- Miner, Nanette. *101 Media and Marketing Tips for the Sole Proprietor.* BVC Publishing, 1998.

Self-Assessment Books

- Bolles, Richard Nelson and Dick Bolles. *2000 What Color Is Your Parachute?* Ten Speed Press, 2000.

- Johnston, Susan. *The Career Adventure: Your Guide to Personal Assessment, Career Exploration and Decision Making*. Prentice Hall, 1998.

- Keyes, Margaret Frings and Mary K. Brown. *Enneagram Relationship Workbook: A Self and Partnership Assessment Guide*. Molysdatur Publications, 1992.

- Nardi, Dario. *Character and Personality Type, Discovering Your Uniqueness for Career and Relationship Success*. Telos Publications, 2000.

- Robbins, Stephen P. *The Prentice Hall Self-Assessment Library: Insights Into Your Skills, Abilities and Interests*. Prentice Hall, 2000.

Goal Setting Books

- Blair, Gary Ryan. *Goal Setting 101: How to Set and Achieve a Goal*. The Goals Guy, 2000.

- Ellis, Keith. *The Magic Lamp, Goal Setting for People Who Hate Setting Goals*. Three Rivers Press, 1998.

- Smith, Douglas K. *Make Success Measurable! A Mindbook-Workbook for Setting Goals and Taking Action*. John Wiley and Sons, 1999.

10
Marketing Materials

1. Review your brainstorming notes from Chapter One (naming your business) and Chapter Nine (self assessment and target marketing definition).

    • What words (adjectives, nouns, verbs, adverbs) best describe the business image you want to project ?

    • Which of your special attributes do you want to highlight in your marketing materials and coaching practice?

    • What are your primary market niches?

    • What words (adjectives, nouns, verbs, adverbs) describe the image or feeling you want to project with your marketing materials?

Elevator Speech

2. Write out your elevator speech. It should be two to four sentences long. If needed, review the example in Chapter Ten of *The Business Of Coaching* (page 132).

3. What variations will you need for different niches? or for more or less time? What aspect will be varied? Write those variations here.

Business Card and Logo

4. How will your business card and logo be designed and created?

   ❑ A professional graphic designer will design and create them, or

   ❑ You will design them and have the graphic designer create them in the computer, or

   ❑ You will design and create them yourself.

Graphic Designer Information and Selection

Name	Contact Info	Cost	References and feedback

Business Card and Logo Design Advance Work

5. Go to local printers and look at sample business cards and logos. Make copies or hand drawings of the elements that you like.

6. Brainstorming Design Elements
   - What shapes do you want to use? Angular or curved, graphics, symbols, images, metaphors?

   - What colors do you want to use? Primaries (red, blue, yellow), pastels, bright, subdued, grayed, vibrant? What colors do you like? What colors support the image you want to project?

- What typeface or font do you like? Script, block letters, freehand, big or small, artsy, classical, whimsical? Review the example font types below and note your thoughts.

  This is the Arial font

  This is the Berkeley font

  ## This is the Lucida Sans font

  This is the Mead Bold font

  This is the Modern No. 20 font

  This is the Monotype Corsiva font

  This is the Parisian font

  This is Times New Roman

7. Go to the library and look at books on logotype, fonts, and logos. Make copies or hand-drawings of the logos and fonts that you like.

8. While at the library, also look at books on business cards and letterhead design. Take notes on any designs that you like.

9. Searching for clip art on the Internet will result in a long list of web sites. Review some of them and note which graphics or designs that you like. Make sure to note the source web address. What additional ideas come to mind?

10. What information will be included on the front of the business card?

11. What information will be printed on the back of the card?

12. How will the business cards be printed?

❑ You will do it yourself

- On basic white stock, or

- On patterned stock

❑ A print shop will do it

Note: Appendix D contains a step-by-step process and tips for submitting and managing a professional print job.

13. Business card and logo computer files

- Keep one copy from the software program in which they were developed.

- Keep copies in .gif and .jpg formats with the highest resolution possible.

- An additional copy of the files will be the "print copy" that the printer will work from.

14. Business Card Worksheet

Brochure

15. What is the target audience for your brochure?

16. How will they receive your brochure? (e.g., from a display, mailed to them with an introductory letter, handed to them at an event)

17. What are the brochure's objectives? What will the reader learn?

18. List the categories of information that you want to include in the brochure. Below are some examples.

   What is coaching?
   Coaching benefits
   Coaching process
   Your coaching philosophy
   Typical / ideal coaching client
   Client testimonials
   Your company vision and mission
   Brief description / bio of you
   Photograph of you
   Contact information
   Sample session offer and description
   Quotes from articles about coaching
   Examples of goals achieved through coaching

Brochure Layout Template

INSIDE PANELS OF BROCHURE

Second panel seen, next to outside panel #1. Might include: • Benefits of coaching • Powerful, short client testimonials • Call to action – why should the reader call you? *Needs to complement outside panel #1.*	**Interior panels** to describe your services, the results, and other information. Might include: • What is a coach? • Coaching benefits • Could you use a coach? • Description of the coaching process • Offer of free sample session • Client testimonials • Your coaching philosophy, mission and vision • Quotes from articles about coaching • Examples of goals achieved through coaching *These panels provide the core info on your services.*

OUTSIDE PANELS OF BROCHURE

First panel seen after opening, next to inside panel #2. Might include: • Business slogan • Provocative saying or quote • Quote from media about coaching • Graphic (if none on cover) *Needs to complement inside panel #2.*	**Last panel reviewed.** Might include: • Your name • All contact info (phone, email, web site address) • Brief bio and description of qualifications • Photo of you *This panel focuses on you, not on coaching.*	**Brochure Cover** Might include: • Business name • Logo • Business slogan • Provocative saying or quote • Graphic (if no logo) • Your name and phone number *Catch their eye! Make them want to read more!*

Introduction Letters

19. What is the target audience for your letter?

20. What is the objective of the letter?

21. What are the key points that you want to convey to the reader?

- Letter introduction key points:

- Main body key points:

- Letter closing key points:

22. What will you offer of value within the letter? For example, a short exercise, self-quiz, sample session gift certificate, article, other.

23. What will you enclose with the letter? For example, your brochure, copies of articles about coaching, flier about an upcoming workshop.

24. To whom will you be sending the letter? List their names here.
    Note: Use good quality paper, envelopes, and printer (i.e. laser printer) for your introductory letters. First impressions are important!

25. Follow-up phone calls:

    ❏   Develop the list of people to call

    ❏   Develop the call script – what will you say?
             Opening information / points:
             Main point / question:
             Wrap-up:

    ❏   Make the calls!

Fliers and Information Sheets

26. What is the objective of the flier?

27. How will you distribute them? For example, by mail, by hand, posted on a bulletin board, by email, on web site.

28. What information will you include on the flier? Typical elements include:

      Headline
      Event description and benefits
      Logistical information and cost
      Presenter bio
      Contact information (to signup or get more info)

29. What type of paper will you use for the flier? (colored paper or designer paper)

30. How will you duplicate the flier? (copy center, or print each one individually)

Web Site

31. How will your web site be developed and posted on the Internet?

    ❑   You will do it yourself

    ❑   You will hire a professional web developer to create and post the site

Web Developer Information and Selection

Name	Contact Info	Cost	References, feedback, web sites checked

Note: Chapter Four contains activities to help you select a web host.

Web Site Design and Development Advance Work

Note: Refer to the Web Site section of Chapter Ten (page 145) in *The Business of Coaching* for additional information and guidance on this topic.

32. What categories of information and specific topics do you want to include in the web site?

    Example categories and topics include:
    - Definition of coaching
    - Typical coaching topics or situations
    - Benefits of coaching
    - Overview of the coaching process
    - Your coaching philosophy, mission, and objectives
    - Specific examples of client benefits from coaching
    - Your bio, including your areas of expertise, qualifications, and education
    - Your photo
    - Client company list (if you provide corporate coaching and have their permission to use the company name)
    - Client testimonials
    - The text of any coaching-related articles (make sure to get the author's written permission first)
    - A calendar of upcoming events
    - Your contact information (phone, fax, email, mailing address)

- What are your "must have" categories or topics?

- What is your "want" list? That is, the categories and topics that you want to include, if possible:

33. Create the text or content for each "must have" category or topic. If possible, use a word processor for ease of modification.

34. Create a paper-based mock-up of the web site, following the directions in Chapter Ten (page 149) of *The Business of Coaching*.

35. What words (adjectives, nouns, verbs) describe the image you want to project with your web site?

36. Make note of the web addresses of any web sites you have seen that you liked.

Web site address	What did you like about this site?

Web Site Development and Design

37. Review the web site design tips found in Chapter Ten of *The Business of Coaching* (starting on page 152)

38. Define web site elements for search engines (work with your developer on this task)

39. Provide your developer with the contact information for your web hosting service provider.

40. Receive web site files from your developer. Make a copy of the files. One copy will be your master file, the other will be your working copy. Make sure to backup these files regularly.

41. Test the web site thoroughly to make sure that each link and menu option works correctly.

Search Engine Registration

42. Who will do the registration?

- ❑   You will do it yourself with individual search engines

- ❑   You will use a search engine registration service

43. Which search engines do you want to be listed on?

44. Which search engine registration service will you use?

Name of Registration Service	Cost for services	Services Offered

10
Additional Resources

Books: General Design

- *The Best of Brochure Design 5*. Rockport Publishers, 1999.

- *The Best of Business Card Design 4*. Rockport Publishers, 2000.

- Carter, David E. *The New Big Book of Logos*. Headbone Interactive, 2000.

- Dover, Caitlin. *Print's Best Letterheads and Business Cards 6*. North Light Books, 2000.

- Finke, Gail Deibler. *Fresh Ideas in Letterhead and Business Card Design 4*. North Light Books, 1999.

- *Letterhead and Logo Design 6*. Rockport Publishers, 1999.

- Miller, Anistatia R. and Jared M. Brown. *What Logos Do And How They Do It*. Rockport Publishers, 1998.

- Parker, Roger C. *One-Minute Designer*. MIS:Press, IDG Books Worldwide, 1997.

- Skaggs, Steven and Sarah Skaggs. *Logos: The Development Of Visual Symbols*. Crisp Publications, 1994.

- Williams, Robin. *The Non-Designer's Design Book*. Peachpit Press, 1994.

- Williams, Robin. *The PC Is Not A Typewriter*. Peachpit Press, 1992.

Books: Writing References

- Andersen, Richard and Helene Hinis. *Write it Right! A Guide For Clear And Correct Writing*. SkillPath Publications, 1993.

- Bayan, Richard. *Words That Sell: The Thesaurus to Help You Promote Your Products, Services, and Ideas*. NTC/Contemporary Publishing, 1987.

- Blumenthal, Lassor A. *The Art of Letter Writing: The New Guide to Writing More Effective Letters for All Occasions*. Perigee, 1986.

- Davidson, Wilma. *Business Writing: What Works, What Won't.* St Martin's Press, 1994.

- Fruehling, Rosemary T. and N.B. Oldham. *Write to the Point!: Letters, Memos, and Reports That Get Results.* McGraw-Hill, 1992.

- Gorssman, Ellie. *The Grammatically Correct Handbook.* Hyperion, 1997.

- Lamb, Sandra E. *How to Write It: A Complete Guide to Everything You'll Ever Write.* Ten Speed Press, 1999.

- May, Debra Hart. *Everyday Letters for Busy People: Hundreds of Sample Letters You Can Copy or Adapt at a Minute's Notice.* Career Press, 1998.

- O'Connor, Patricia. *Words Fail Me – What Everyone Who Writes Should Know About Writing.* Harcourt Brace, 1999.

- Roman, Kenneth and Joel Raphaelson. *Writing That Works: How to Improve Your Memos, Letters, Reports, Speeches, Resumes, Plans, and Other Business Papers.* Harper Mass Market Paperbacks, 1995.

- Shertzer, Margaret. *The Elements of Grammar.* MacMillan Publishing Company, 1986.

- Strunk, William Jr. and E.B. White. *The Elements Of Style.* MacMillan Publishing Company, 1979.

Editorial Resources

- Editorial Freelancers Association: www.the-efa.org

- Indiana University has a copyediting listserv with a listing of freelance copyeditors at http://ce-l.blinn.com/freelance.html

- One recommended freelance, part-time copyeditor is Howard Daniel, Pen-for-Rent: (808) 262-4297, howard@pen4rent.com, www.freeagent.com/Pen4Rent

Copyright Information

- Library of Congress: (202) 707-3000; www.loc.gov/copyright/

Books: Desktop Publishing

- Green, Chuck. *The Desktop Publisher's Idea Book: One-Of-A-Kind Projects, Expert Tips, and Hard-To-Find Sources.* Random House, 1997.

- Parker, Roger C. *Desktop Publishing & Design for Dummies*. IDG Books Worldwide, 1995.

Books: Web Design Books

- Dornfest, Asha. *FrontPage 2000 For Dummies*. IDG Books Worldwide, 1999.

- Matthews, Martin S. and Erik B. Poulsen. *FrontPage 2000: The Complete Reference*. Osborne McGraw-Hill, 1999.

- Niederst, Jennifer and Richard Koman. *Web Design in a Nutshell: A Desktop Quick Reference*. O'Reilly & Associates, 1998.

- Stanek, William B. and William Robert Stanek. *Microsoft FrontPage 2000 Unleashed*. Sams, 1999.

- Web Presence Coaching and Consulting Services. A 20-30% discount is available for ICF members. Contact Lee Keller, (813) 969-3614, lee@bizanswers.com, and www.bizanswers.com.

- Webmasters Toolbox: www.marionia.com/toolbox (Contains free resources for design and promotion of web sites)

- www.dsiegel.com/tips: Web design tips

Software: Desktop Publishing

- Adobe Illustrator 9.0 (vector graphics creation for web or print): $400

- Adobe PageMaker 6.5 (professional page layout): $500

- Adobe Photoshop 6.0 (image editing tools): $600

- Jasc PaintShop Pro 7.0: $100

- Macromedia FreeHand 10: $500

- Microsoft Publisher 2000: $90

Web Design Books and Software

- Allaire HomeSite 4.5: $100

- Macromedia Dreamweaver 4.0: $300

- Microsoft FrontPage 2000: $150

Sources for Paper (business cards, brochures, fliers, letterhead)

- Avery Dennison Corp: www.avery.com

- Desktop Supplies: www.desktopsupplies.com

- Idea Art – Promotional Papers for Desktop Printers: (800) 433-2278; www.ideaart.com (under construction at time of printing)

- Paper Access: (800) paper-01; www.paperaccess.com

- PaperDirect Inc.: (800) 272-7377; www.paperdirect.com

- Paper Plus: (800) 943-3649; www.4paperplus.com

Low-cost or Free Search Engine Registration and Resources

- Deadlock Design (www.deadlock.com) has a excellent tutorial on search engine registration in the section titled "The Art of Business Web Site Promotion." There is also an informative piece on getting a listing on Yahoo!

- Internet Promotion Services: www.Netpromote.com

- Microsoft bCentral SubmitIt! Registration service: http://submitit.bcentral.com/

- RegisterIt service: http://websitegarage.netscape.com

- Search engine tips and resources: www.searchenginewatch.com

- Web site Register: www.website-register.com

- WebStep: www.mmgexpress.com (registration service)

Domain Name Registration

- www.networksolutions.com

- www.register.com

Miscellaneous

- The Coaching News, the International Coach Federation's monthly electronic newsletter lists recent articles published about coaching (and those written by ICF members). Sign up at www.coachfederation.org or (888) 423-3131

11
Effective Networking

1. Review your notes from Chapter Nine. What are your primary market niches?

Potential Networking Venues

2. What networking organizations would expose you to your chosen niches?

Organization	When / Where meet	Cost?	Contact Info

Networking Preparation

3. Before the Event

   ☐ Business cards

   ☐ Elevator speech for introductions

   - Short version

   - Longer version

   ☐ Answer ready for "What do you do?"

   ☐ Answer ready for "What is coaching?"

   ☐ Answers rehearsed, with attention to body language and tone

   ☐ Powerful questions selected and rehearsed

   ☐ Familiarity with the organization's mission and objective

   ☐ Confirmation of meeting date, time, and place

4. At the Event

   ☐ Arrive early and stay late

   ☐ Introduce yourself

   ☐ Be a coach: listen and ask questions

   ☐ Talk about yourself and coaching

   ☐ Try to relax even if you are feeling nervous

   ☐ Offer something of value

   ☐ Offer sample sessions

   ☐ Get business cards, make notes of items promised and about the person

5. After the Event

   ❑ Send off promised information

   ❑ Schedule sample sessions

   ❑ Thank-you notes to others you met

   ❑ Any other items of value to send to your networking contacts?

   ❑ Follow up phone calls after information mailed out

   ❑ Ask people out for coffee or lunch to learn more about what they do and get advice on what you do

   ❑ Get involved with the organization – volunteer, be visible and active

11
Additional Resources

Various Associations, Organizations and Related Resources

- American Association of University Women: www.aauw.org; (800) 326-AAUW

- American Business Women's Association: www.abwa.org; (816) 361-6621

- Business Women's Network: www.bwni.com

- Elite Leads: www.eliteleads.com

- International Chamber of Commerce search site: http://clickcity.com/index2.htm

- International Coach Federation: www.coachfederation.org

- Kiwanis International: www.kiwanis.org

- Leads Clubs: (800) 783-3761

- LeTip leads clubs: www.letip.com

- National Association of Female Executives: www.nafe.com; (800) 634-NAFE

- Look in your local yellow pages for other groups, typically listed under Associations, Business and Trade Organizations, or Professional Organizations. Examples include: Rotary Club, Lions, Soroptimist Club, League of Women Voters, Junior League, Special Olympics, United Way, and other service, civic, or charitable organizations.

- Reference books at your library:

  - *National Trade and Professional Associations of the United States*. Edited by Downs, Bausch, and White. Columbia Books, 2000

  - *Encyclopedia of Associations*. Gale Research, 2000. Three volumes.

Networking Books and Resources

- Fine, Debra. *The Fine Art of Small Talk: How to Start a Conversation, Keep It Going, Build Rapport – And Leave a Positive Impression.* Career Track Publications, 1997 (Audio Cassette).

- Garner, Alan. *Conversationally Speaking: Tested New Ways to Increase Your Personal and Social Effectiveness.* Lowell House, 1997.

- RoAne, Susan. *What Do I Say Next: Talking Your Way to Business and Social Success.* Time Warner Audio Books, 1997.

- RoAne, Susan. *The Secrets of Savvy Networking: How to Make the Best Connections for Business and Personal Success.* Warner Books, 1993.

- RoAne, Susan. *How to Work a Room : Learn the Strategies of Savvy Socializing – For Business and Personal Success.* Warner Books, 1989.

Communication Related Books

- Bienvenu, Sherron. *The Presentation Skills Workshop: Helping People Create and Deliver Great Presentations* (The Trainer's Workshop Series). Amacom, 1999.

- Maysonave, Sherry. *Casual Power: How to Power Up Your Nonverbal Communication & Dress Down for Success.* Bright Books Inc., 1999.

- Molloy, John T. *John T. Molloy's New Dress for Success.* Warner Books, 1988.

- Molloy, John T. *New Women's Dress for Success.* Warner Books, 1996.

- Wainwright, Gordon. *Body Language.* Teach Yourself, 2000.

Around the Office

We lift ourselves by our thought, we climb upon our vision of ourselves. If you want to enlarge your life, you must first enlarge your thought of it and of yourself. Hold the ideal of yourself as you long to be, always, everywhere – your ideal of what you long to attain – the ideal of health, efficiency, success.

ORISON SWETT MARDEN

12: Transition to Self-Employment
- The Structure of Work
- Work Schedule
- Time Management
- Increasing Efficiency
- Addressing Procrastination

13: Managing the Paperwork
- Why Keep It
- What Type of Information
- Where to Store It
- When to Process It
- Record Retention

14: Equipping Your Office
- Telephone and Headset
- Messaging
- Personal Computer
- Printers and Fax Machine
- Office Ergonomics

12
The Transition to Self-Employment

Work-Related Structures and Schedule

1. List the work-related structures that your previous jobs have provided. Some example categories are listed below.

    Work week:

    Work day:

    Distractions allowed:

    Goals:

    Location of work:

    Acceptable behavior:

    Nearby amenities:

2. How many hours per week do you want to work on your coaching business?

    - How many hours on client appointments? (Recommend allotting 45 minutes for each 30 minute session.)

    - How many hours on marketing, administrative, financial and other non-billable activities? (Recommended minimum of four to ten hours a week.)

3. What days and hours will you work?

Day	Work Hours
Monday	
Tuesday	
Wednesday	
Thursday	
Friday	
Saturday	
Sunday	

4. Other considerations in your work structure:

- How will you dress for work?

- When will you break for lunch?

- Will you have breaks during the day? If so, how many and when?

- What interruptions or distractions will you allow in your workday? Examples might include turning on the TV, doing household chores, walking the dog or personal phone calls. Will there be a time limit on these events?

- Will you snack during your work time? If yes, at what times?

- Under what circumstances will you take off a morning, afternoon, or day?

Time Management

Note: Review the time management model on pages 174 to 180 in *The Business Of Coaching.*

5. Review the business goals you established in Chapter Nine. Of these goals, which four to six goals do you want to focus on for this year?

-

-

-

-

-

-

6. For each of your goals, make a list of the tasks or activities needed to achieve that goal. Use the worksheet below as a template.

Description of Goal:

Task	Preceding Task Number(s)	Priority (H, M, L)	Target Completion Date
1.			
2.			
3.			
4.			
5.			
6.			
7.			
8.			
9.			
10.			
11.			
12.			

An example worksheet is on the following page.

Example Prioritized Task List

GOAL:

Enroll 10 new clients into my practice within the next five months. (High Priority)

TASKS:

1. On a daily basis, visualize the practice with 10 more clients. (High, target date = November 30)

2. Get the current coach training schedule. (High; target date = July 1)

3. Sign up for remaining training courses. (High; target date = August 1; first need to complete #2)

4. Call my targeted networking venues to get schedules for upcoming events. (High; target date = July 1)

5. Attend at least one networking event each week. Meet three new people at each event. Follow up with each one after the event. (High; target date = July through September; first need to complete #4)

6. Offer sample sessions to five new people each week. (High; target date = July through September)

7. Buy a book on brochure design and purchase the brochure paper. (Medium; target date = August)

8. Develop and send out a letter and brochure to my friends, colleagues and family members. Ask for referrals and offer sample sessions. (Medium; target date = July)

9. Make a contact at a radio station to see if they need any radio program hosts. (Low; target date = November)

10. Complete the coach certification program. (Medium; target date = April of next year; first need to complete #3)

7. Combine the tasks across all of your goals into one big list. Then, develop a monthly task list using the priority and target deadlines as your guide. Use the following template and group similar tasks together (for example, phone calls, items to purchase, research to conduct).

Month of: _____

Task	Priority	Group	Done?
1.			
2.			
3.			
4.			
5.			
6.			
7.			
8.			
9.			
10.			
11.			
12.			

8. Based on your monthly activities list and your appointments, develop a daily to-do list using the following template. Group similar tasks together (for example, phone calls, items to purchase, research to conduct) to use time most efficiently.

Day of: _____

Task or Activity	Priority	Group	Done?
1.			
2.			
3.			
4.			
5.			
6.			
7.			
8.			
9.			
10.			
11.			
12.			
13.			
14.			
15.			

9. Now that you know what types of activities are on your task lists, and your weekly work schedule, you can develop a generic weekly schedule. Use the format below. An example generic schedule is on the following page.

Day	Generic Schedule
Monday	Morning: Afternoon: Evening:
Tuesday	Morning: Afternoon: Evening:
Wednesday	Morning: Afternoon: Evening:
Thursday	Morning: Afternoon: Evening:
Friday	Morning: Afternoon: Evening:
Saturday	Morning: Afternoon: Evening:
Sunday	Morning: Afternoon: Evening:

Example Generic Weekly Schedule

Monday	AM: Volunteer at Sally's daycare
	PM: Off
	Evening: Networking meetings

Monday   AM: Volunteer at Sally's daycare
                PM: Off
                Evening: Networking meetings

Tuesday   AM: Phone calls and email
                PM: Dan's soccer games

Wednesday   AM: Coaching sessions
                PM: Run errands

Thursday   AM: Coaching sessions
                PM: Work on marketing materials

Friday   AM: Breakfast networking meeting
                PM: Finances, paperwork, and email
                Evening: Date night with Chris

Saturday   Off all day

Sunday   AM: Church
                PM: Catch up on reading and filing

Evaluate Your Progress

10. At the end of each month, evaluate the effectiveness of your monthly plan and to-do list.

   - Which tasks were you able to complete? Check them off your list and celebrate your success!

   - Which tasks were you not able to complete?

Task	Reasons for missed target date	New target date	New priority

   - How will you adjust your plan and to-do list to increase the likelihood that you will accomplish all your target tasks?

12
Additional Resources

Time Management and Goal Setting Resources

- Blair, Gary Ryan. *Goal Setting 101: How to Set and Achieve a Goal.* The Goals Guy, 2000.

- Ellis, Keith. *The Magic Lamp, Goal Setting for People Who Hate Setting Goals.* Three Rivers Press, 1998.

- Fettke, Rich. *Focus: A Guide To Clarity And Achievement.* Audio cassette. The Fettke Group, 1998.

- Lakein, Alan. *How To Get Control Of Your Time And Your Life.* New American Library, 1996.

- Morgenstern, Julie. *Time Management From The Inside Out: The Foolproof System For Taking Control Of Your Schedule And Your Life.* Henry Holt, 2000.

- Richardson, Cheryl. *Take Time For Your Life: A Complete Program For Getting Your Life Into Balance And Honoring Your True Priorities.* Audio cassette. Sounds True, 1999.

- Smith, Douglas K. *Make Success Measurable! A Mindbook-Workbook for Setting Goals and Taking Action.* John Wiley and Sons, 1999.

- http://onhealth.webmd.com/lifestyle - Search for "time management"

- www.cyberquotations.com/articles.htm - Information on goal setting, time management, and success

- www.mindtools.com - Time management, goal setting, planning, stress management

- www.salesleaders.com - Time management, sales tips, motivational

- www.stresstips.com - Tips for stress management

- www.topachievement.com/goalsetting.htm - Goal setting

Calendar Products

- At-A-Glance: www.ataglance.com

- DayRunner: www.dayrunner.com

- DayTimer (paper and software): www.daytimer.com

- Franklin Covey: www.franklincovey.com

- Handheld training teleclasses: Heather Davis, HD Coaching; heather@Hdcoaching.com or palmcoaching@hotmail.com

- Handspring Visor: www.handspring.com

- Lotus Organizer 6.0: www.lotus.com/home.nsf/welcome/organizer

- Microsoft Outlook: www.microsoft.com/office/outlook

- Palm Pilot: www.palm.com

- PDA Buzz – Top PDA and Handheld PC News: www.pdabuzz.com

- Visual Day Planner 7.0: www.inklineglobal.net/products/vdp/

Books on Fear by Susan Jeffers

- *Feel The Fear And Do It Anyway*. Fawcett Books, 1992.

- *Feel The Fear .. And Beyond: Mastering The Techniques For Doing It Anyway*. Random House, 1998.

Speed Reading Books (increases efficiency!)

- Frank, Stanley D. *Evelyn Wood 7-Day Speed Reading And Learning Program: Remember Everything You Read*. Avon, 1992.

- Kump, Peter. *Breakthrough Rapid Reading*. Prentice Hall Press, 1998.

- Ostrov, Rick. *Absolute Speed Reading With Power Reading*. Education Press, 1978.

13
Managing the Paperwork

Why Keep It

1. Throw away all the paper and information that you don't need. Clear out the clutter! When in doubt about keeping something, ask yourself the following questions:

   - What will I use it for?

   - When will I need it?

   - Under what circumstances might I need it?

   - What would happen if I didn't have it?

What Type of Information

2. Each piece of information has one of four different purposes. Classify your remaining files into one of these four categories.

   - *Current* information that is time sensitive – keep close at hand

   - *Reference* materials and resources – keep nearby

   - *Master* documents that are used for duplication – keep nearby

   - *Archive* information that contains historical data – can be stored farther away from your office

3. What storage locations do you have available to you:

   - Close at hand (that is, by your work desk)

   - Close to your work area (such as a nearby bookcase or file cabinets)

   - Farther away from your office, and out of the way (for example in attic space or an empty closet)

4. Using the table below (and referring to the example table on the next page)

❏ Define your file categories and topics

❏ Classify your information into types: current, resource, master, archive

❏ Determine what location(s) the information will be stored in.

Category or Topic	Type	Storage Location(s)

Example File Categories and Purposes

Category and Topics	Current	Reference	Master	Archive
Coaching				
Intake packet			✔	
Exercises			✔	
Client files	✔			✔
Potential client file	✔			
Books		✔		
Articles		✔	✔	
Marketing				
Masters (e.g., brochure, fliers)			✔	
Goals and plans	✔			✔
Business cards received	✔			✔
Sample marketing materials		✔		
Current projects	✔			
Mailing list	✔			
Networking calendar	✔			
Financial and Legal				
Client billing records	✔			✔
Accounts payable (bills)	✔			✔
Budget	✔			✔
Receipts	✔			✔
Account statements	✔			✔
Tax forms	✔			✔
Business docs (e.g., EIN, Articles of Org.)		✔		
Tax info; books and articles		✔		

Where To Store It

5. Set up your physical locations:

- At your desk: file cabinet, desktop file holder, computer

  ❑ Colored folders for each category

  ❑ Clearly labeled folders

  ❑ Use of file jackets and file pockets where needed

  ❑ Use of folders with built-in pockets for diskettes where needed

  ❑ Business card file

  ❑ Contact management software installed (if desired)

  ❑ Mailing list software installed (if desired)

  ❑ To-Do file

  ❑ Monthly tickler files

  ❑ Receipt basket and accordion file

  ❑ Other:

- On your computer, set up a directory structure that will make it easy for you to store and retrieve your files. An example structure is presented on the following page.

Example Computer Directory Structure

My-Company-Name (would be at the top directory level)
Coaching
Intake packet
Client contract file.doc
Balance wheel.ppt
Values exercise.doc
Other files
Exercises
Project files
Marketing
Masters
Project files
Goals and actions
Mailing list
Finance and legal
Client invoices
Budget
Tax files
Biz documents
Workshop projects
Life In Balance
Getting Organized
Archive (would contain previous versions or old files)
Coaching
Marketing
Finance and legal
Workshop projects

- At your reading location, set up a space for your books, magazines, and journals. Locate a recycle bin nearby.

- In the general vicinity of your office (bookcase and filing cabinet), set up locations for your resource materials and master files.

   What locations have you set up?

- Create a storage location for your archive files, e.g., client records, financial records, tax forms, past planning documents. Files should be put in boxes in date order or by category. Boxes should be clearly marked with contents, storage date and disposal date. Note: Refer to the record retention guidelines in Chapter Thirteen (page 197) in *The Business Of Coaching* to determine how long you should keep specific types of records.

   What locations have you set up?

   What information do you have in your archive files?

Topic	Box Number	Date Stored	Destroy Date

When to Process It

6. Create your schedule for daily, weekly, monthly, quarterly, semi-annual, and annual activities.

   - Refer to the example calendar below to help create your own schedule. A blank schedule form can be found after the example calendar.

   - Make sure to update your task lists (monthly, daily) with these tasks and to mark the dates on your calendar!

Example Calendar for Processing Information

Interval	Activity	Day
Daily	Create daily to-do list	Morning
	Sort all papers and email into four categories: 1. Throw it away or recycle 2. Send it on someone else 3. Act on it right away 4. File it in a topic file, or for future reading, or in the accounts payable folder, or in the appropriate tickler file	Ongoing
	File expense receipts in the receipt basket	Evening
Weekly	Update contact management software and/or mailing list with new contacts or information from networking events.	Fri. aft
	Catch up on reading materials. Recycle, file with resources, or pull out articles to file or for action.	Sun. eve
	Weekly filing catch-up	Sun. eve
Monthly	Enter receipts into the financial management program	1st Fri.
	Receive client payments and deposit	1st Fri.
	Update the budget with actual expenses for the past month. Review budget for needed modification.	1st Fri.
	Create client invoices	3rd Fri.
	Review business and marketing goals and monthly to-do list. Prepare list for following month.	3rd Fri.

Quarterly	Run Profit and Loss report for the quarter	1st Sat.
	Compute and pay estimated taxes (federal and state). Due Jan 15, April 15, June 15, Sept 15	1st Sat. of four months

Semi-annual		
	Develop high-level budget for first six months of following year	2nd Fri June
	Develop high-level budget for months 7–12 of next year	2nd Fri Dec.
	Develop new marketing goals and plans for following six months	2nd Fri Dec. and June
	Review all marketing materials for any needed modifications	2nd Fri Dec. and June

Annual		
	Close out current annual budget with actual expenses	4th Fri Jan.
	Run annual Profit and Loss report	4th Fri Jan.
	Send out 1099s (if necessary)	4th Sat Jan.
	Compute and pay business taxes, federal and state	Second half Feb.
	Archive tax files, federal and state	March
	Dispose of archive files that have passed required holding period	March
	Review insurance coverage for needed modification	March
	Annual goal setting for business and marketing. Develop and prioritize task list. Create to-do list for January.	Dec.

Use the blank template on the next two pages to create your own schedule.

Notes:

Information Processing Calendar

Interval	Activity	Day
Daily	Create daily to-do list	Morning
Weekly		
Monthly		

Quarterly		
Semi-annual		
Annual		

13
Additional Resources

Office Organizing Books and Web sites

- http://organizedhome.com

- www.123sortit.com

- www.bitsmith.com/resource/office.htm

- www.organized-living.com

- www.organizerswebring.com

- www.wco.com/~dpmiller/

- Jogerst, Karen and Lindy Schneider. *If I Could Just Get Organized! : Home Management Hope for Pilers and Filers*. Rubies Publishing, 1999.

- Kolberg, Judith. *Conquering Chronic Disorganization*. Squall Press, 1999.

- Lockwood, Georgene. *The Complete Idiot's Guide to Organizing Your Life*. MacMillan Distribution, 1999.

- Morgenstern, Julie. *Organizing from the Inside Out: The Foolproof System for Organizing Your Home, Your Office and Your Life*. Owl Books, 1998.

- Schlenger, Sunny and Roberta Roesch. *How To Get Organized In Spite Of Yourself: Time and Space Management That Works With Your Personal Style*. Signet, 1999.

Contact Management and Mailing List Software

- ACT! 2000 5.0; Interact Commerce Corp, $170

- GoldMine 5.0; GoldMine Software, $170

- Mail List; MySoftware, $10

- Maximizer 5.0; Multiactive Software, $125

- Microsoft Outlook; Microsoft, $110

- My Advanced Maillist; MySoftware, $35

Office Supplies

- Office Depot: www.officedepot.com

- Office Max: www.officemax.com

- Penny Wise Office Products: www.penny-wise.com (discount for ICF members)

- Staples: www.staples.com

14
Equipping Your Office

Use the following tables to assist you in your equipment shopping and purchase decisions.

Office Telephone

Features	Model	Model	Model
Model/Brand Name:			
Cost:			
One- or two-line phone			
Cordless phone			
Headset jack			
Mute button			
Adjustable ring volume			
Automatic redial			
Hold			
Call-on-hold indicator			
Last number redial			
Speed dial or programmable memory keys			
Caller ID display			
Conferencing ability			

Telephone Headset

Brand and model number of the telephone you use:

Features	Model	Model	Model
Model/Brand Name:			
Cost:			
Uses headset jack			
Size of jack plug needed			
Uses amplifier			
Single ear			
Double ear			
Corded			
Cordless			
Noise-canceling microphone			
Comfort			
Other:			
Other:			

Telephone Answering Machine

Features	Model	Model	Model
Model/Brand Name:			
Cost:			
Battery back-up			
Clarity of outgoing message			
Variable length incoming message so the caller doesn't get cut off (voice activated or VOX setting)			
Ring selector			
Toll-saver feature			
30 minutes or greater total record time			
Lets the caller know if the machine is full			
Able to skip and store messages			
Easy remote access for message retrieval and for re-recording the outgoing message			
Call counter			
Date- and time-stamp on each message			
Obvious, easy-to-reach and use controls			
Other:			
Other:			

Personal Computer

Features	Model	Model	Model
Model/Brand Name:			
Base Cost:			
Processor chip speed			
Hard drive size			
Warranty period			
Cost to upgrade to 64 or 128 MB RAM			
Cost to upgrade to 17" monitor			
Cost to upgrade to 19" monitor			
Ethernet card (for DSL or cable modem)			
V90 modem (also known as a 56K modem)			
ZIP drive			
CD writer			
JAZ drive			
Second internal hard drive			
Other:			
Other:			
Other:			
Other:			

Printers

Features	Model	Model	Model
Model/Brand Name:			
Cost:			
Laser or Ink Jet			
Pages per minute – B&W			
Page per minute – Color			
Resolution: dots per inch (DPI)			
Draft mode option			
Sheet feeder			
Duplex printing (both sides)			
Compatible with your computer operating system			
Controls easy to reach and use			
Warranty period			
Other:			

Fax Machines

Features	Model	Model	Model
Model/Brand Name:			
Cost:			
Uses plain paper			
Resolution: dots per inch (DPI)			
Resolution settings for standard, fine, very fine, photo			
Speed dial/memory			
Auto redial if busy			
Sheet feeder			
Easy to reach and use controls			
Separate handset			
Warranty period			
Other:			

Office Chair

Features	Model	Model	Model
Model/Brand Name:			
Cost:			
Back support (up or down, tilt forward or back)			
Lumbar support (more or less, up or down)			
Arm rests (height and angle)			
Height of seat			
Tilt of seat (knees up or down)			
Ability to rock			
Thighs horizontal when feet flat on the floor			
Comfortable in a variety of positions			
Color			
Other:			

14
Additional Resources

Headsets

- GBH Distributing: www.gbh.com; (800) 222-5425. Offers discounts for ICF members.

- Headsets.com: www.headsets.com

- Hello Direct: www.hellodirect.com

- Midwest Teletron: www.mwteletron.com; (800) 827-9715. Offers discounts for ICF members.

- Plantronics: www.plantronics.com

Computer Manufacturers

- Apple: www.apple.com

- Compaq: www.compaq.com

- Dell: www.dell.com

- Gateway: www.gateway.com

- Hewlett - Packard: www.hp.com

Office Supplies and Small Electronics/Accessories

- Office Depot: www.officedepot.com

- Office Max: www.officemax.com

- Penny Wise Office Products: www.penny-wise.com (discount for ICF members)

- Staples: www.staples.com

Computer and Electronics Online Magazines

- http://macworld.zdnet.com

- www.smalloffice.com (Central web site for both Home Office Computing and Small Business Computing)

- www.winmag.com

- www.zdnet.com/pcmag

Ergonomics Resources

- Heller, Alison. *Your Guide To Office Ergonomic Furniture and Accessories.* Worksite International, 2000. (888) 288-4463, www.insitept.com

- Linden, Paul. *Comfort @ Your Computer: Body Awareness Training for Pain-Free Computer Use.* North Atlantic Books, 2000.

- http://onhealth.webmd.com/conditions/home - Search for "home office"

- www.stanford.edu/dept/EHS/work/ergo

- www.pc.ibm/ww/healthycomputing/we-intro.html

Office Layout and Design

- Zimmerman, Neal. *Home Office Design: Everything You Need To Know About Planning, Organizing and Furnishing Your Work Space.* John Wiley and Sons, 1996.

Appendices

A: General Small Business Resources

B: Coaching Resources

C: Copies of Commonly Used, Business Related IRS Tax Forms

D: Managing a Professional Print Job

General Small Business Resources

- MSN Money Central: http://moneycentral.msn.com

- www.allbusiness.com

- www.bizoffice.com

- www.bizresource.com

- www.business.gov (U.S. Business Advisor)

- www.businessknowhow.com

- www.entrepreneur.com

- www.home-business-central.com

- www.irs.gov

- www.isquare.com (Small Business Advisor)

- www.morebusiness.com

- www.quicken.com/small_business

- www.sba.gov (Small Business Administration)

- www.sba.gov/sbdc (Small Business Development Centers)

- www.score.org (SCORE: Service Corps of Retired Executives)

- www.smalloffice.com

- www.wordweb.org (Women's Online Resource Directory)

- www.workingsolo.com

APPENDIX B

Coaching Resources

Books

- Crane, Thomas G. *The Heart of Coaching: Using Transformational Coaching to Create a High-Performance Culture*. FTA Press, 1998.

- Carson, Richard David and Novie Rogers. *Taming Your Gremlin: A Guide to Enjoying Yourself*. HarperCollins, 1986.

- Flaherty, James. *Coaching Evoking Excellence in Others*. Butterworth-Heinemann, 1998.

- Hargrove, Robert. *Masterful Coaching: Extraordinary Results by Impacting People and the Way They Think and Work Together*. Pfeiffer & Co., 1995.

- Leonard, Thomas J. *Becoming A Coach: The Coach U Approach*. Coach U Press, 1999.

- Leonard, Thomas J. and Byron Larson. *The Portable Coach: 28 Surefire Strategies for Business and Personal Success*. Scribner, 1998.

- Whitworth, Laura and Henry House, Phil Sandahl, Henry Kimsey-House. *Co-Active Coaching: New Skills for Coaching People Toward Success in Work and Life*. Davies-Black Publishing, 1998.

Web Sites

- www.coachesportal.com

- www.peer.ca/coaching.html

- International Coach Federation (ICF): www.coachfederation.org. ICF is a nonprofit, professional organization of personal and business coaches that exists to "build, support, and preserve the integrity of the coaching profession."

Coaching Schools

Although there are over coaching forty schools, only nine are currently classified as an Accredited Coach Training Program by the International Coach Federation (ICF). This information is current as of the print date. For a complete listing of all the schools, plus links to their web pages, review the "Coach Training Schools" section under the "General Information" category in the International Coach Federation web site (www.coachfederation.org).

Accredited Coaching Training Programs:

- Academy for Coach Training: Bellvue, WA; (800) 897-8707; www.coachtraining.com

- Coach 21 Co., Ltd.: Tokyo, Japan; +81-3-3237-9781; www.coacha.com

- Coach For Life: San Diego, CA; (888) 262-2446; www.coachforlife.com

- Coach U: Steamboat Springs, CO; (800) 48Coach; www.coachu.com

- The Coaches Training Institute: San Rafael, CA; (800) 691-6008; www.thecoaches.com

- Corporate Coach U Intl.: Steamboat Springs, CO; (888) 391-2740; www.ccui.com

- The Newfield Network, USA, LLC: Olney, MD; (301) 570-6680; www.newfieldnetwork.com

- New Ventures West: San Francisco, CA; (800) 332-4618; www.newventureswest.com

- Success Unlimited Network: Reston, VA; (703) 716-8374; www.successunlimitednet.com

Copies of IRS Business-Related Tax Forms

List of Forms Included:

- 1040-Schedule C, Tax Return for Sole Proprietor

- 1040-Schedule C-EZ, Tax Return for Sole Proprietor

- 1065, Partnership Informational Return and associated K-1 form

- 1120-S, Tax Return for S-Corporation and associated K-1 form

- 1040-ES, Estimated Payments

- 8829, Home Office Business Expense

- SS-4, Application for an Employer Identification Number

- 1096, Annual Summary of 1099s

- 1099-MISC, Miscellaneous Income

Note:

- ➤ These copies may not include the complete form or the instructions. Please download the entire form and instructions from the IRS web site at www.irs.gov, or by calling (800) TAX-FORM.
- ➤ For forms 1096 and 1099, you cannot file a downloaded form due to special ink and computer coding on the form. Call the IRS to order copies of these forms.

SCHEDULE C
(Form 1040)

Department of the Treasury
Internal Revenue Service   (99)

Profit or Loss From Business
(Sole Proprietorship)

▶ Partnerships, joint ventures, etc., must file Form 1065 or Form 1065-B.

▶ Attach to Form 1040 or Form 1041.   ▶ See Instructions for Schedule C (Form 1040).

OMB No. 1545-0074

2001

Attachment
Sequence No. **09**

Name of proprietor | Social security number (SSN)

A Principal business or profession, including product or service (see page C-1 of the instructions) | **B** Enter code from pages C-7 & 8 ▶

C Business name. If no separate business name, leave blank. | **D** Employer ID number (EIN), if any

E Business address (including suite or room no.) ▶ ....
City, town or post office, state, and ZIP code

F Accounting method: **(1)** ☐ Cash **(2)** ☐ Accrual **(3)** ☐ Other (specify) ▶ ....

G Did you "materially participate" in the operation of this business during 2001? If "No," see page C-2 for limit on losses . ☐ Yes ☐ No

H If you started or acquired this business during 2001, check here . . . . ▶ ☐

Part I   Income

1	Gross receipts or sales. **Caution.** If this income was reported to you on Form W-2 and the "Statutory employee" box on that form was checked, see page C-2 and check here . . . . . . ▶ ☐	1	
2	Returns and allowances	2	
3	Subtract line 2 from line 1	3	
4	Cost of goods sold (from line 42 on page 2)	4	
5	**Gross profit.** Subtract line 4 from line 3	5	
6	Other income, including Federal and state gasoline or fuel tax credit or refund (see page C-3) . . .	6	
7	**Gross income.** Add lines 5 and 6 . . . . ▶	7	

Part II   Expenses. Enter expenses for business use of your home **only** on line 30.

8	Advertising	8		19	Pension and profit-sharing plans	19	
9	Bad debts from sales or services (see page C-3) . .	9		20	Rent or lease (see page C-4):		
				a Vehicles, machinery, and equipment .	20a	
10	Car and truck expenses (see page C-3)	10		**b** Other business property . .	20b	
11	Commissions and fees . .	11		21	Repairs and maintenance . .	21	
12	Depletion	12		22	Supplies (not included in Part III) .	22	
13	Depreciation and section 179 expense deduction (not included in Part III) (see page C-3) . .	13		23	Taxes and licenses	23	
				24	Travel, meals, and entertainment:		
				a Travel	24a	
14	Employee benefit programs (other than on line 19) . . .	14		**b** Meals and entertainment		
15	Insurance (other than health) .	15		**c** Enter nondeductible amount included on line 24b (see page C-5) .		
16	Interest:						
a	Mortgage (paid to banks, etc.) .	16a		**d** Subtract line 24c from line 24b .	24d	
b	Other	16b		25	Utilities	25	
17	Legal and professional services	17		26	Wages (less employment credits) .	26	
18	Office expense	18		27	Other expenses (from line 48 on page 2)	27	

28	**Total expenses** before expenses for business use of home. Add lines 8 through 27 in columns . ▶	28	
29	Tentative profit (loss). Subtract line 28 from line 7	29	
30	Expenses for business use of your home. Attach **Form 8829**	30	
31	**Net profit or (loss).** Subtract line 30 from line 29.		

- If a profit, enter on **Form 1040, line 12,** and **also** on **Schedule SE, line 2** (statutory employees, see page C-5). Estates and trusts, enter on Form 1041, line 3.
- If a loss, you **must** go to line 32.

	31

32 If you have a loss, check the box that describes your investment in this activity (see page C-6).

- If you checked 32a, enter the loss on **Form 1040, line 12,** and **also** on **Schedule SE, line 2** (statutory employees, see page C-5). Estates and trusts, enter on Form 1041, line 3.
- If you checked 32b, you **must** attach **Form 6198.**

32a ☐ All investment is at risk.
32b ☐ Some investment is not at risk.

For Paperwork Reduction Act Notice, see Form 1040 instructions.   Cat. No. 11334P   Schedule C (Form 1040) 2001

Part III   Cost of Goods Sold (see page C-6)

33   Method(s) used to
     value closing inventory: **a** ☐ Cost   **b** ☐ Lower of cost or market   **c** ☐ Other (attach explanation)

34   Was there any change in determining quantities, costs, or valuations between opening and closing inventory? If
     "Yes," attach explanation . . . . ☐ **Yes**   ☐ **No**

35 Inventory at beginning of year. If different from last year's closing inventory, attach explanation . .	**35**	
36 Purchases less cost of items withdrawn for personal use	**36**	
37 Cost of labor. Do not include any amounts paid to yourself	**37**	
38 Materials and supplies	**38**	
39 Other costs	**39**	
40 Add lines 35 through 39	**40**	
41 Inventory at end of year	**41**	
42 **Cost of goods sold.** Subtract line 41 from line 40. Enter the result here and on page 1, line 4 . .	**42**	

Part IV   Information on Your Vehicle. Complete this part **only** if you are claiming car or truck expenses on line 10 and are not required to file Form 4562 for this business. See the instructions for line 13 on page C-3 to find out if you must file.

43   When did you place your vehicle in service for business purposes? (month, day, year) ▶ ..../............/....... .

44   Of the total number of miles you drove your vehicle during 2001, enter the number of miles you used your vehicle for:

a Business .... **b** Commuting .... **c** Other ....

45   Do you (or your spouse) have another vehicle available for personal use? . . . . ☐ **Yes**   ☐ **No**

46   Was your vehicle available for personal use during off-duty hours?   . . . . ☐ **Yes**   ☐ **No**

47a Do you have evidence to support your deduction?   . . . . ☐ **Yes**   ☐ **No**

  b If "Yes," is the evidence written? . . . . ☐ **Yes**   ☐ **No**

Part V   Other Expenses. List below business expenses not included on lines 8–26 or line 30.

--		
--		
--		
--		
--		
--		
--		
--		
48 **Total other expenses.** Enter here and on page 1, line 27	**48**	

SCHEDULE C-EZ
(Form 1040)

Department of the Treasury
Internal Revenue Service   (99)

Net Profit From Business
(Sole Proprietorship)

▶ Partnerships, joint ventures, etc., must file Form 1065 or 1065-B.

▶ Attach to Form 1040 or 1041.   ▶ See instructions on back.

OMB No. 1545-0074

2001

Attachment
Sequence No. **09A**

Name of proprietor

Social security number (SSN)

Part I   General Information

You May Use Schedule C-EZ Instead of Schedule C Only If You:

- Had business expenses of $2,500 or less.
- Use the cash method of accounting.
- Did not have an inventory at any time during the year.
- Did not have a net loss from your business.
- Had only one business as a sole proprietor.

And You:

- Had no employees during the year.
- Are not required to file **Form 4562,** Depreciation and Amortization, for this business. See the instructions for Schedule C, line 13, on page C-3 to find out if you must file.
- Do not deduct expenses for business use of your home.
- Do not have prior year unallowed passive activity losses from this business.

A Principal business or profession, including product or service

B Enter code from pages C-7 & 8 ▶

C Business name. If no separate business name, leave blank.

D Employer ID number (EIN), if any

E Business address (including suite or room no.). Address not required if same as on Form 1040, page 1.

City, town or post office, state, and ZIP code

Part II   Figure Your Net Profit

1 Gross receipts. **Caution.** If this income was reported to you on Form W-2 and the "Statutory employee" box on that form was checked, see **Statutory Employees** in the instructions for Schedule C, line 1, on page C-2 and check here . . . . ▶ ☐ | **1** |

2 Total expenses. If more than $2,500, you **must** use Schedule C. See instructions . . . . . | **2** |

3 Net profit. Subtract line 2 from line 1. If less than zero, you **must** use Schedule C. Enter on **Form 1040, line 12,** and **also** on **Schedule SE, line 2.** (Statutory employees **do not** report this amount on Schedule SE, line 2. Estates and trusts, enter on Form 1041, line 3.) . . . . . | **3** |

Part III   Information on Your Vehicle. Complete this part **only** if you are claiming car or truck expenses on line 2.

4 When did you place your vehicle in service for business purposes? (month, day, year) ▶ .... / .... / ....

5 Of the total number of miles you drove your vehicle during 2001, enter the number of miles you used your vehicle for:

a Business ....   **b** Commuting ....   **c** Other ....

6 Do you (or your spouse) have another vehicle available for personal use? . . . .   ☐ Yes   ☐ No

7 Was your vehicle available for personal use during off-duty hours? . . . .   ☐ Yes   ☐ No

8a Do you have evidence to support your deduction? . . . .   ☐ Yes   ☐ No

b If "Yes," is the evidence written? . . . .   ☐ Yes   ☐ No

For Paperwork Reduction Act Notice, see Form 1040 instructions.   Cat. No. 14374D   Schedule C-EZ (Form 1040) 2001

Instructions

You may use Schedule C-EZ instead of Schedule C if you operated a business or practiced a profession as a sole proprietorship and you have met all the requirements listed in Part I of Schedule C-EZ.

Line A

Describe the business or professional activity that provided your principal source of income reported on line 1. Give the general field or activity and the type of product or service.

Line B

Enter the six-digit code that identifies your principal business or professional activity. See pages C-7 and C-8 of the Instructions for Schedule C for the list of codes.

Line D

You need an employer identification number (EIN) only if you had a qualified retirement plan or were required to file an employment, excise, estate, trust, or alcohol, tobacco, and firearms tax return. If you need an EIN, file **Form SS-4,** Application for Employer Identification Number. If you do not have an EIN, leave line D blank. **Do not** enter your SSN.

Line E

Enter your business address. Show a street address instead of a box number. Include the suite or room number, if any.

Line 1

Enter gross receipts from your trade or business. Include amounts you received in your trade or business that were properly shown on **Forms 1099-MISC.** If the total amounts that were reported in box 7 of Forms 1099-MISC are more than the total you are reporting on line 1, attach a statement explaining the difference. You must show all items of taxable income actually or constructively received during the year (in cash, property, or services). Income is constructively received when it is credited to your account or set aside for you to use. Do not offset this amount by any losses.

Line 2

Enter the total amount of all deductible business expenses you actually paid during the year. Examples of these expenses include advertising, car and truck expenses, commissions and fees, insurance, interest, legal and professional services, office expense, rent or lease expenses, repairs and maintenance, supplies, taxes, travel, the allowable percentage of business meals and entertainment, and utilities (including telephone). For details, see the instructions for Schedule C, Parts II and V, on pages C-3 through C-6. If you wish, you may use the optional worksheet below to record your expenses.

If you claim car or truck expenses, be sure to complete Part III of Schedule C-EZ.

Optional Worksheet for Line 2 (keep a copy for your records)

a Business meals and entertainment	a		
b Enter nondeductible amount included on line **a** (see the instructions for lines 24b and 24c on page C-5)	b		
c Deductible business meals and entertainment. Subtract line **b** from line **a**	c	
d	d	
e	e	
f	f	
g	g	
h	h	
i	i	
j **Total.** Add lines **c** through **i.** Enter here and on line 2	j	

Form **1065**	**U.S. Return of Partnership Income**	OMB No. 1545-0099
Department of the Treasury Internal Revenue Service	For calendar year 2001, or tax year beginning .... , 2001, and ending .... , 20.... . ▶ See separate instructions.	**2001**

A Principal business activity	Use the IRS label. Other-wise, print or type.	Name of partnership	**D** Employer identification number
B Principal product or service		Number, street, and room or suite no. If a P.O. box, see page 13 of the instructions.	**E** Date business started
C Business code number		City or town, state, and ZIP code	**F** Total assets (see page 14 of the instructions) $

G Check applicable boxes: **(1)** ☐ Initial return **(2)** ☐ Final return **(3)** ☐ Name change **(4)** ☐ Address change **(5)** ☐ Amended return

H Check accounting method: **(1)** ☐ Cash **(2)** ☐ Accrual **(3)** ☐ Other (specify) ▶ ....

I Number of Schedules K-1. Attach one for each person who was a partner at any time during the tax year ▶ ....

Caution: *Include **only** trade or business income and expenses on lines 1a through 22 below. See the instructions for more information.*

Income

1a	Gross receipts or sales	**1a**	
b	Less returns and allowances	**1b**	**1c**
2	Cost of goods sold (Schedule A, line 8)		**2**
3	Gross profit. Subtract line 2 from line 1c		**3**
4	Ordinary income (loss) from other partnerships, estates, and trusts *(attach schedule)*		**4**
5	Net farm profit (loss) *(attach Schedule F (Form 1040))*		**5**
6	Net gain (loss) from Form 4797, Part II, line 18		**6**
7	Other income (loss) *(attach schedule)*		**7**
8	**Total income (loss).** Combine lines 3 through 7		**8**

Deductions (see page 15 of the instructions for limitations)

9	Salaries and wages (other than to partners) (less employment credits)		**9**
10	Guaranteed payments to partners		**10**
11	Repairs and maintenance		**11**
12	Bad debts		**12**
13	Rent		**13**
14	Taxes and licenses		**14**
15	Interest		**15**
16a	Depreciation (if required, attach Form 4562)	**16a**	
b	Less depreciation reported on Schedule A and elsewhere on return	**16b**	**16c**
17	Depletion **(Do not deduct oil and gas depletion.)**		**17**
18	Retirement plans, etc.		**18**
19	Employee benefit programs		**19**
20	Other deductions *(attach schedule)*		**20**
21	**Total deductions.** Add the amounts shown in the far right column for lines 9 through 20		**21**
22	**Ordinary income (loss)** from trade or business activities. Subtract line 21 from line 8		**22**

Sign Here

Under penalties of perjury, I declare that I have examined this return, including accompanying schedules and statements, and to the best of my knowledge and belief, it is true, correct, and complete. Declaration of preparer (other than general partner or limited liability company member) is based on all information of which preparer has any knowledge.

▶ _____
Signature of general partner or limited liability company member

▶ _____ Date

May the IRS discuss this return with the preparer shown below (see instructions)? ☐ Yes ☐ No

Paid Preparer's Use Only	Preparer's signature		Date	Check if self-employed ▶ ☐	Preparer's SSN or PTIN
	Firm's name (or yours if self-employed), address, and ZIP code ▶			EIN ▶	
				Phone no. ( )	

For Paperwork Reduction Act Notice, see separate instructions.   Cat. No. 11390Z   Form **1065** (2001)

Schedule A   Cost of Goods Sold (see page 18 of the instructions)

1 Inventory at beginning of year	1
2 Purchases less cost of items withdrawn for personal use	2
3 Cost of labor.	3
4 Additional section 263A costs *(attach schedule)*	4
5 Other costs *(attach schedule)*	5
6 **Total.** Add lines 1 through 5	6
7 Inventory at end of year	7
8 **Cost of goods sold.** Subtract line 7 from line 6. Enter here and on page 1, line 2	8

9a   Check all methods used for valuing closing inventory:

   (i) ☐ Cost as described in Regulations section 1.471-3

   (ii) ☐ Lower of cost or market as described in Regulations section 1.471-4

   (iii) ☐ Other (specify method used and attach explanation) ▶ ....

   b Check this box if there was a writedown of "subnormal" goods as described in Regulations section 1.471-2(c). . . . ▶ ☐

   c Check this box if the LIFO inventory method was adopted this tax year for any goods *(if checked, attach Form 970)* . . ▶ ☐

   d Do the rules of section 263A (for property produced or acquired for resale) apply to the partnership? . . ☐ **Yes** ☐ **No**

   e Was there any change in determining quantities, cost, or valuations between opening and closing inventory? ☐ **Yes** ☐ **No**
   If "Yes," attach explanation.

Schedule B   Other Information

	Yes	No
1 What type of entity is filing this return? Check the applicable box:		
a ☐ Domestic general partnership **b** ☐ Domestic limited partnership		
c ☐ Domestic limited liability company **d** ☐ Domestic limited liability partnership		
e ☐ Foreign partnership **f** ☐ Other ▶		
2 Are any partners in this partnership also partnerships?		
3 During the partnership's tax year, did the partnership own any interest in another partnership or in any foreign entity that was disregarded as an entity separate from its owner under Regulations sections 301.7701-2 and 301.7701-3? If yes, see instructions for required attachment		
4 Is this partnership subject to the consolidated audit procedures of sections 6221 through 6233? If "Yes," see **Designation of Tax Matters Partner** below		
5 Does this partnership meet **all three** of the following requirements?		
a The partnership's total receipts for the tax year were less than $250,000;		
b The partnership's total assets at the end of the tax year were less than $600,000; **and**		
c Schedules K-1 are filed with the return and furnished to the partners on or before the due date (including extensions) for the partnership return.		
If "Yes," the partnership is not required to complete Schedules L, M-1, and M-2; Item F on page 1 of Form 1065; or Item J on Schedule K-1		
6 Does this partnership have any foreign partners? If "Yes," the partnership may have to file Forms 8804, 8805 and 8813. See page 20 of the instructions		
7 Is this partnership a publicly traded partnership as defined in section 469(k)(2)?		
8 Has this partnership filed, or is it required to file, **Form 8264,** Application for Registration of a Tax Shelter? . .		
9 At any time during calendar year 2001, did the partnership have an interest in or a signature or other authority over a financial account in a foreign country (such as a bank account, securities account, or other financial account)? See page 20 of the instructions for exceptions and filing requirements for Form TD F 90-22.1. If "Yes," enter the name of the foreign country. ▶		
10 During the tax year, did the partnership receive a distribution from, or was it the grantor of, or transferor to, a foreign trust? If "Yes," the partnership may have to file Form 3520. See page 20 of the instructions		
11 Was there a distribution of property or a transfer (e.g., by sale or death) of a partnership interest during the tax year? If "Yes," you may elect to adjust the basis of the partnership's assets under section 754 by attaching the statement described under **Elections Made By the Partnership** on page 8 of the instructions		
12 Enter the number of Forms 8865 attached to this return . . . . ▶		

Designation of Tax Matters Partner (see page 20 of the instructions)

Enter below the general partner designated as the tax matters partner (TMP) for the tax year of this return:

Name of designated TMP ▶	Identifying number of TMP ▶
Address of designated TMP ▶	

Schedule K — Partners' Shares of Income, Credits, Deductions, etc.

	(a) Distributive share items		(b) Total amount
Income (Loss)	**1** Ordinary income (loss) from trade or business activities (page 1, line 22)	**1**	
	2 Net income (loss) from rental real estate activities (attach Form 8825)	**2**	
	3a Gross income from other rental activities **3a**		
	b Expenses from other rental activities (attach schedule) **3b**		
	c Net income (loss) from other rental activities. Subtract line 3b from line 3a	**3c**	
	4 Portfolio income (loss): **a** Interest income	**4a**	
	b Ordinary dividends	**4b**	
	c Royalty income	**4c**	
	d Net short-term capital gain (loss) (attach Schedule D (Form 1065))	**4d**	
	e (1) Net long-term capital gain (loss) (attach Schedule D (Form 1065))	**4e(1)**	
	(2) 28% rate gain (loss) ▶ .... **(3)** Qualified 5-year gain ▶		
	f Other portfolio income (loss) (attach schedule)	**4f**	
	5 Guaranteed payments to partners	**5**	
	6 Net section 1231 gain (loss) (other than due to casualty or theft) (attach Form 4797)	**6**	
	7 Other income (loss) (attach schedule)	**7**	
Deductions	**8** Charitable contributions (attach schedule)	**8**	
	9 Section 179 expense deduction (attach Form 4562)	**9**	
	10 Deductions related to portfolio income (itemize)	**10**	
	11 Other deductions (attach schedule)	**11**	
Credits	**12a** Low-income housing credit:		
	(1) From partnerships to which section 42(j)(5) applies	**12a(1)**	
	(2) Other than on line 12a(1)	**12a(2)**	
	b Qualified rehabilitation expenditures related to rental real estate activities (attach Form 3468)	**12b**	
	c Credits (other than credits shown on lines 12a and 12b) related to rental real estate activities	**12c**	
	d Credits related to other rental activities	**12d**	
	13 Other credits	**13**	
Invest-ment Interest	**14a** Interest expense on investment debts	**14a**	
	b (1) Investment income included on lines 4a, 4b, 4c, and 4f above	**14b(1)**	
	(2) Investment expenses included on line 10 above	**14b(2)**	
Self-Employ-ment	**15a** Net earnings (loss) from self-employment	**15a**	
	b Gross farming or fishing income	**15b**	
	c Gross nonfarm income	**15c**	
Adjustments and Tax Preference Items	**16a** Depreciation adjustment on property placed in service after 1986	**16a**	
	b Adjusted gain or loss	**16b**	
	c Depletion (other than oil and gas)	**16c**	
	d (1) Gross income from oil, gas, and geothermal properties	**16d(1)**	
	(2) Deductions allocable to oil, gas, and geothermal properties	**16d(2)**	
	e Other adjustments and tax preference items (attach schedule)	**16e**	
Foreign Taxes	**17a** Name of foreign country or U.S. possession ▶		
	b Gross income from all sources	**17b**	
	c Gross income sourced at partner level	**17c**	
	d Foreign gross income sourced at partnership level:		
	(1) Passive ▶ .... **(2)** Listed categories (attach schedule) ▶ .... **(3)** General limitation ▶	**17d(3)**	
	e Deductions allocated and apportioned at partner level:		
	(1) Interest expense ▶ .... **(2)** Other	**17e(2)**	
	f Deductions allocated and apportioned at partnership level to foreign source income:		
	(1) Passive ▶ .... **(2)** Listed categories (attach schedule) ▶ .... **(3)** General limitation ▶	**17f(3)**	
	g Total foreign taxes (check one): ▶ Paid ☐ Accrued ☐	**17g**	
	h Reduction in taxes available for credit (attach schedule)	**17h**	
Other	**18** Section 59(e)(2) expenditures: **a** Type ▶ .... **b** Amount ▶	**18b**	
	19 Tax-exempt interest income	**19**	
	20 Other tax-exempt income	**20**	
	21 Nondeductible expenses	**21**	
	22 Distributions of money (cash and marketable securities)	**22**	
	23 Distributions of property other than money	**23**	
	24 Other items and amounts required to be reported separately to partners (attach schedule)		

Analysis of Net Income (Loss)

1 Net income (loss). Combine Schedule K, lines 1 through 7 in column (b). From the result, subtract the sum of Schedule K, lines 8 through 11, 14a, 17g, and 18b **1**

2 Analysis by partner type:

	(i) Corporate	(ii) Individual (active)	(iii) Individual (passive)	(iv) Partnership	(v) Exempt organization	(vi) Nominee/Other
a General partners						
b Limited partners						

Schedule L — Balance Sheets per Books (Not required if Question 5 on Schedule B is answered "Yes.")

Assets	Beginning of tax year (a)	(b)	End of tax year (c)	(d)
1 Cash				
2a Trade notes and accounts receivable				
b Less allowance for bad debts				
3 Inventories				
4 U.S. government obligations				
5 Tax-exempt securities				
6 Other current assets (attach schedule)				
7 Mortgage and real estate loans				
8 Other investments (attach schedule)				
9a Buildings and other depreciable assets				
b Less accumulated depreciation				
10a Depletable assets				
b Less accumulated depletion				
11 Land (net of any amortization)				
12a Intangible assets (amortizable only)				
b Less accumulated amortization				
13 Other assets (attach schedule)				
14 Total assets				
Liabilities and Capital				
15 Accounts payable				
16 Mortgages, notes, bonds payable in less than 1 year				
17 Other current liabilities (attach schedule)				
18 All nonrecourse loans				
19 Mortgages, notes, bonds payable in 1 year or more				
20 Other liabilities (attach schedule)				
21 Partners' capital accounts				
22 Total liabilities and capital				

Schedule M-1 — Reconciliation of Income (Loss) per Books With Income (Loss) per Return
(Not required if Question 5 on Schedule B is answered "Yes.")

1 Net income (loss) per books
2 Income included on Schedule K, lines 1 through 4, 6, and 7, not recorded on books this year (itemize):
3 Guaranteed payments (other than health insurance)
4 Expenses recorded on books this year not included on Schedule K, lines 1 through 11, 14a, 17g, and 18b (itemize):
  a Depreciation $
  b Travel and entertainment $
5 Add lines 1 through 4

6 Income recorded on books this year not included on Schedule K, lines 1 through 7 (itemize):
  a Tax-exempt interest $
7 Deductions included on Schedule K, lines 1 through 11, 14a, 17g, and 18b, not charged against book income this year (itemize):
  a Depreciation $
8 Add lines 6 and 7
9 Income (loss) (Analysis of Net Income (Loss), line 1). Subtract line 8 from line 5

Schedule M-2 — Analysis of Partners' Capital Accounts (Not required if Question 5 on Schedule B is answered "Yes.")

1 Balance at beginning of year
2 Capital contributed during year
3 Net income (loss) per books
4 Other increases (itemize):
5 Add lines 1 through 4

6 Distributions: a Cash
                 b Property
7 Other decreases (itemize):
8 Add lines 6 and 7
9 Balance at end of year. Subtract line 8 from line 5

SCHEDULE K-1
(Form 1065)
Department of the Treasury
Internal Revenue Service

Partner's Share of Income, Credits, Deductions, etc.
▶ See separate instructions.

For calendar year 2001 or tax year beginning   , 2001, and ending   , 20

OMB No. 1545-0099

2001

Partner's identifying number ▶

Partnership's identifying number ▶

Partner's name, address, and ZIP code

Partnership's name, address, and ZIP code

A This partner is a ☐ general partner   ☐ limited partner
     ☐ limited liability company member

B What type of entity is this partner? ▶ ....

C Is this partner a ☐ domestic or a ☐ foreign partner?

	(i) Before change or termination	(ii) End of year

D Enter partner's percentage of:
Profit sharing . . . . % .... %
Loss sharing . . . . % .... %
Ownership of capital . . . . % .... %

E IRS Center where partnership filed return:

F Partner's share of liabilities (see instructions):
Nonrecourse . . . . $ ....
Qualified nonrecourse financing . $ ....
Other . . . . $ ....

G Tax shelter registration number . ▶ ....

H Check here if this partnership is a publicly traded partnership as defined in section 469(k)(2) . . . . . ☐

I Check applicable boxes: **(1)** ☐ Final K-1 **(2)** ☐ Amended K-1

J Analysis of partner's capital account:

(a) Capital account at beginning of year	(b) Capital contributed during year	(c) Partner's share of lines 3, 4, and 7, Form 1065, Schedule M-2	(d) Withdrawals and distributions	(e) Capital account at end of year (combine columns (a) through (d))
			( )	

(a) Distributive share item	(b) Amount	(c) 1040 filers enter the amount in column (b) on:

Income (Loss)

1 Ordinary income (loss) from trade or business activities . . .	**1**	See page 6 of Partner's Instructions for Schedule K-1 (Form 1065).
2 Net income (loss) from rental real estate activities	**2**	
3 Net income (loss) from other rental activities	**3**	
4 Portfolio income (loss):		
a Interest	**4a**	Sch. B, Part I, line 1
b Ordinary dividends	**4b**	Sch. B, Part II, line 5
c Royalties	**4c**	Sch. E, Part I, line 4
d Net short-term capital gain (loss)	**4d**	Sch. D, line 5, col. (f)
e (1) Net long-term capital gain (loss).	**4e(1)**	Sch. D, line 12, col. (f)
(2) 28% rate gain (loss)	**4e(2)**	Sch. D, line 12, col. (g)
(3) Qualified 5-year gain	**4e(3)**	Line 4 of worksheet for Sch. D, line 29
f Other portfolio income (loss) *(attach schedule)*	**4f**	Enter on applicable line of your return.
5 Guaranteed payments to partner	**5**	See page 6 of Partner's Instructions for Schedule K-1 (Form 1065).
6 Net section 1231 gain (loss) (other than due to casualty or theft)	**6**	
7 Other income (loss) *(attach schedule)*	**7**	Enter on applicable line of your return.

Deductions

8 Charitable contributions (see instructions) *(attach schedule)* . .	**8**	Sch. A, line 15 or 16
9 Section 179 expense deduction.	**9**	See pages 7 and 8 of Partner's Instructions for Schedule K-1 (Form 1065).
10 Deductions related to portfolio income *(attach schedule)* . . .	**10**	
11 Other deductions *(attach schedule)*.	**11**	

Credits

12a Low-income housing credit:		Form 8586, line 5
(1) From section 42(j)(5) partnerships	**12a(1)**	
(2) Other than on line 12a(1)	**12a(2)**	
b Qualified rehabilitation expenditures related to rental real estate activities	**12b**	
c Credits (other than credits shown on lines 12a and 12b) related to rental real estate activities.	**12c**	See page 8 of Partner's Instructions for Schedule K-1 (Form 1065).
d Credits related to other rental activities	**12d**	
13 Other credits.	**13**	

For Paperwork Reduction Act Notice, see Instructions for Form 1065.   Cat. No. 11394R   **Schedule K-1 (Form 1065) 2001**

	(a) Distributive share item		(b) Amount	(c) 1040 filers enter the amount in column (b) on:
Investment Interest	**14a**	Interest expense on investment debts	**14a**	Form 4952, line 1
	b	**(1)** Investment income included on lines 4a, 4b, 4c, and 4f . .	**14b(1)**	⎱ See page 9 of Partner's Instructions for Schedule K-1 (Form 1065).
		(2) Investment expenses included on line 10	**14b(2)**	
Self-employment	**15a**	Net earnings (loss) from self-employment	**15a**	Sch. SE, Section A or B
	b	Gross farming or fishing income	**15b**	⎱ See page 9 of Partner's Instructions for Schedule K-1 (Form 1065).
	c	Gross nonfarm income	**15c**	
Adjustments and Tax Preference Items	**16a**	Depreciation adjustment on property placed in service after 1986	**16a**	⎫
	b	Adjusted gain or loss	**16b**	See page 9 of Partner's Instructions for Schedule K-1 (Form 1065) and Instructions for Form 6251.
	c	Depletion (other than oil and gas)	**16c**	
	d	**(1)** Gross income from oil, gas, and geothermal properties . .	**16d(1)**	
		(2) Deductions allocable to oil, gas, and geothermal properties	**16d(2)**	
	e	Other adjustments and tax preference items *(attach schedule)*	**16e**	⎭
Foreign Taxes	**17a**	Name of foreign country or U.S. possession ▶ -----------------		⎫
	b	Gross income from all sources	**17b**	
	c	Gross income sourced at partner level	**17c**	
	d	Foreign gross income sourced at partnership level:		
		(1) Passive	**17d(1)**	
		(2) Listed categories *(attach schedule)*	**17d(2)**	
		(3) General limitation	**17d(3)**	
	e	Deductions allocated and apportioned at partner level:		Form 1116, Part I
		(1) Interest expense	**17e(1)**	
		(2) Other	**17e(2)**	
	f	Deductions allocated and apportioned at partnership level to foreign source income:		
		(1) Passive	**17f(1)**	
		(2) Listed categories *(attach schedule)*	**17f(2)**	
		(3) General limitation	**17f(3)**	⎭
	g	Total foreign taxes (check one): ▶ ☐ Paid ☐ Accrued . . .	**17g**	Form 1116, Part II
	h	Reduction in taxes available for credit *(attach schedule)* . . .	**17h**	Form 1116, line 12
Other	**18**	Section 59(e)(2) expenditures: **a** Type ▶ -----------------		⎱ See page 9 of Partner's Instructions for Schedule K-1 (Form 1065).
	b	Amount	**18b**	
	19	Tax-exempt interest income	**19**	Form 1040, line 8b
	20	Other tax-exempt income	**20**	⎫
	21	Nondeductible expenses	**21**	See pages 9 and 10 of Partner's Instructions for Schedule K-1 (Form 1065).
	22	Distributions of money (cash and marketable securities) . . .	**22**	
	23	Distributions of property other than money	**23**	⎭
	24	Recapture of low-income housing credit:		
	a	From section 42(j)(5) partnerships	**24a**	⎱ Form 8611, line 8
	b	Other than on line 24a	**24b**	
Supplemental Information	**25**	Supplemental information required to be reported separately to each partner *(attach additional schedules if more space is needed):*		

Form **1120S**

Department of the Treasury
Internal Revenue Service

U.S. Income Tax Return for an S Corporation

▶ Do not file this form unless the corporation has timely filed
Form 2553 to elect to be an S corporation.
▶ See separate instructions.

OMB No. 1545-0130

2001

For calendar year 2001, or tax year beginning _____ , 2001, and ending _____ , 20____

A Effective date of election as an S corporation	Use IRS label. Other-wise, print or type.	Name
		Number, street, and room or suite no. (If a P.O. box, see page 11 of the instructions.)
B Business code no. (see pages 29–31)		City or town, state, and ZIP code

C Employer identification number

D Date incorporated

E Total assets (see page 11)
$ _____

F Check applicable boxes:　(1) ☐ Initial return　(2) ☐ Final return　(3) ☐ Name change　(4) ☐ Address change　(5) ☐ Amended return
G Enter number of shareholders in the corporation at end of the tax year . . . . ▶

Caution: Include **only** trade or business income and expenses on lines 1a through 21. See page 11 of the instructions for more information.

Income

1a	Gross receipts or sales _____ **b** Less returns and allowances _____ **c** Bal ▶	**1c**	
2	Cost of goods sold (Schedule A, line 8)	**2**	
3	Gross profit. Subtract line 2 from line 1c	**3**	
4	Net gain (loss) from Form 4797, Part II, line 18 (attach Form 4797) . . .	**4**	
5	Other income (loss) (attach schedule).	**5**	
6	**Total income (loss).** Combine lines 3 through 5 . . . . ▶	**6**	

Deductions (see page 12 of the instructions for limitations)

7	Compensation of officers	**7**	
8	Salaries and wages (less employment credits)	**8**	
9	Repairs and maintenance	**9**	
10	Bad debts	**10**	
11	Rents.	**11**	
12	Taxes and licenses	**12**	
13	Interest	**13**	
14a	Depreciation (if required, attach Form 4562) . . . **14a**		
b	Depreciation claimed on Schedule A and elsewhere on return . . **14b**		
c	Subtract line 14b from line 14a	**14c**	
15	Depletion **(Do not deduct oil and gas depletion.)**	**15**	
16	Advertising	**16**	
17	Pension, profit-sharing, etc., plans	**17**	
18	Employee benefit programs.	**18**	
19	Other deductions (attach schedule)	**19**	
20	**Total deductions.** Add the amounts shown in the far right column for lines 7 through 19 . ▶	**20**	
21	Ordinary income (loss) from trade or business activities. Subtract line 20 from line 6. . . .	**21**	

Tax and Payments

22	**Tax:　a** Excess net passive income tax (attach schedule) . . . **22a**		
b	Tax from Schedule D (Form 1120S) **22b**		
c	Add lines 22a and 22b (see page 16 of the instructions for additional taxes) . . .	**22c**	
23	**Payments: a** 2001 estimated tax payments and amount applied from 2000 return **23a**		
b	Tax deposited with Form 7004. . . . . . . **23b**		
c	Credit for Federal tax paid on fuels (attach Form 4136) **23c**		
d	Add lines 23a through 23c	**23d**	
24	Estimated tax penalty. Check if Form 2220 is attached . . . . ▶ ☐	**24**	
25	**Tax due.** If the total of lines 22c and 24 is larger than line 23d, enter amount owed. See page 4 of the instructions for depository method of payment . . . . ▶	**25**	
26	**Overpayment.** If line 23d is larger than the total of lines 22c and 24, enter amount overpaid ▶	**26**	
27	Enter amount of line 26 you want: **Credited to 2002 estimated tax** ▶ _____ Refunded ▶	**27**	

Sign Here

Under penalties of perjury, I declare that I have examined this return, including accompanying schedules and statements, and to the best of my knowledge and belief, it is true, correct, and complete. Declaration of preparer (other than taxpayer) is based on all information of which preparer has any knowledge.

▶ _____　　▶ _____
Signature of officer　　　Date　　　　　Title

May the IRS discuss this return with the preparer shown below (see instructions)? ☐ **Yes** ☐ **No**

Paid Preparer's Use Only

Preparer's signature ▶		Date	Check if self-employed ☐	Preparer's SSN or PTIN
Firm's name (or yours if self-employed), address, and ZIP code ▶			EIN	
			Phone no. (　　)	

For Paperwork Reduction Act Notice, see the separate instructions.　　Cat. No. 11510H　　Form **1120S** (2001)

Schedule A — Cost of Goods Sold (see page 16 of the instructions)

1	Inventory at beginning of year	1
2	Purchases	2
3	Cost of labor	3
4	Additional section 263A costs *(attach schedule)*	4
5	Other costs *(attach schedule)*	5
6	**Total.** Add lines 1 through 5	6
7	Inventory at end of year	7
8	**Cost of goods sold.** Subtract line 7 from line 6. Enter here and on page 1, line 2	8

9a Check all methods used for valuing closing inventory:
  (i) ☐ Cost as described in Regulations section 1.471-3
  (ii) ☐ Lower of cost or market as described in Regulations section 1.471-4
  (iii) ☐ Other (specify method used and attach explanation) ▶ ------------------------
b Check if there was a writedown of "subnormal" goods as described in Regulations section 1.471-2(c) ▶ ☐
c Check if the LIFO inventory method was adopted this tax year for any goods *(if checked, attach Form 970)* ▶ ☐
d If the LIFO inventory method was used for this tax year, enter percentage (or amounts) of closing inventory computed under LIFO | 9d |
e Do the rules of section 263A (for property produced or acquired for resale) apply to the corporation? ☐ Yes ☐ No
f Was there any change in determining quantities, cost, or valuations between opening and closing inventory? ☐ Yes ☐ No
  If "Yes," attach explanation.

Schedule B — Other Information — Yes | No

1 Check method of accounting: **(a)** ☐ Cash **(b)** ☐ Accrual **(c)** ☐ Other (specify) ▶ --------------------
2 Refer to the list on pages 29 through 31 of the instructions and state the corporation's principal:
  (a) Business activity ▶ -------------------- **(b)** Product or service ▶ --------------------
3 Did the corporation at the end of the tax year own, directly or indirectly, 50% or more of the voting stock of a domestic corporation? (For rules of attribution, see section 267(c).) If "Yes," attach a schedule showing: **(a)** name, address, and employer identification number and **(b)** percentage owned.
4 Was the corporation a member of a controlled group subject to the provisions of section 1561?
5 Check this box if the corporation has filed or is required to file **Form 8264,** Application for Registration of a Tax Shelter ▶ ☐
6 Check this box if the corporation issued publicly offered debt instruments with original issue discount ▶ ☐
  If so, the corporation may have to file **Form 8281,** Information Return for Publicly Offered Original Issue Discount Instruments.
7 If the corporation: **(a)** filed its election to be an S corporation after 1986, **(b)** was a C corporation before it elected to be an S corporation **or** the corporation acquired an asset with a basis determined by reference to its basis (or the basis of any other property) in the hands of a C corporation, and **(c)** has net unrealized built-in gain (defined in section 1374(d)(1)) in excess of the net recognized built-in gain from prior years, enter the net unrealized built-in gain reduced by net recognized built-in gain from prior years (see page 17 of the instructions) ▶ $ --------------
8 Check this box if the corporation had accumulated earnings and profits at the close of the tax year (see page 17 of the instructions) ▶ ☐

Note: *If the corporation had assets or operated a business in a foreign country or U.S. possession, it may be required to attach Schedule N (Form 1120), Foreign Operations of U.S. Corporations, to this return. See Schedule N for details.*

Schedule K — Shareholders' Shares of Income, Credits, Deductions, etc.

	(a) Pro rata share items		(b) Total amount
Income (Loss)	1 Ordinary income (loss) from trade or business activities (page 1, line 21)		1
	2 Net income (loss) from rental real estate activities *(attach Form 8825)*		2
	3a Gross income from other rental activities	3a	
	b Expenses from other rental activities *(attach schedule)*	3b	
	c Net income (loss) from other rental activities. Subtract line 3b from line 3a		3c
	4 Portfolio income (loss):		
	a Interest income		4a
	b Ordinary dividends		4b
	c Royalty income		4c
	d Net short-term capital gain (loss) *(attach Schedule D (Form 1120S))*		4d
	e (1) Net long-term capital gain (loss) *(attach Schedule D (Form 1120S))*		4e(1)
	(2) 28% rate gain (loss) ▶ -------------- (3) Qualified 5-year gain ▶--------------		
	f Other portfolio income (loss) *(attach schedule)*		4f
	5 Net section 1231 gain (loss) (other than due to casualty or theft) *(attach Form 4797)*		5
	6 Other income (loss) *(attach schedule)*		6

Schedule K   Shareholders' Shares of Income, Credits, Deductions, etc. (*continued*)

	(a) Pro rata share items		(b) Total amount	
Deductions	**7** Charitable contributions (*attach schedule*)	**7**		
	8 Section 179 expense deduction (*attach Form 4562*)	**8**		
	9 Deductions related to portfolio income (loss) (itemize)	**9**		
	10 Other deductions (*attach schedule*)	**10**		
Investment Interest	**11a** Interest expense on investment debts	**11a**		
	b (1) Investment income included on lines 4a, 4b, 4c, and 4f above	**11b(1)**		
	(2) Investment expenses included on line 9 above	**11b(2)**		
Credits	**12a** Credit for alcohol used as a fuel (*attach Form 6478*)	**12a**		
	b Low-income housing credit:			
	(1) From partnerships to which section 42(j)(5) applies	**12b(1)**		
	(2) Other than on line 12b(1)	**12b(2)**		
	c Qualified rehabilitation expenditures related to rental real estate activities (*attach Form 3468*)	**12c**		
	d Credits (other than credits shown on lines 12b and 12c) related to rental real estate activities	**12d**		
	e Credits related to other rental activities	**12e**		
	13 Other credits	**13**		
Adjustments and Tax Preference Items	**14a** Depreciation adjustment on property placed in service after 1986	**14a**		
	b Adjusted gain or loss	**14b**		
	c Depletion (other than oil and gas)	**14c**		
	d (1) Gross income from oil, gas, or geothermal properties	**14d(1)**		
	(2) Deductions allocable to oil, gas, or geothermal properties	**14d(2)**		
	e Other adjustments and tax preference items (*attach schedule*)	**14e**		
Foreign Taxes	**15a** Name of foreign country or U.S. possession ▶ _____			
	b Gross income from all sources	**15b**		
	c Gross income sourced at shareholder level	**15c**		
	d Foreign gross income sourced at corporate level:			
	(1) Passive	**15d(1)**		
	(2) Listed categories (*attach schedule*)	**15d(2)**		
	(3) General limitation	**15d(3)**		
	e Deductions allocated and apportioned at shareholder level:			
	(1) Interest expense	**15e(1)**		
	(2) Other	**15e(2)**		
	f Deductions allocated and apportioned at corporate level to foreign source income:			
	(1) Passive	**15f(1)**		
	(2) Listed categories (*attach schedule*)	**15f(2)**		
	(3) General limitation	**15f(3)**		
	g Total foreign taxes (check one): ▶ ☐ Paid ☐ Accrued	**15g**		
	h Reduction in taxes available for credit (*attach schedule*)	**15h**		
Other	**16** Section 59(e)(2) expenditures: **a** Type ▶ _____ **b** Amount ▶	**16b**		
	17 Tax-exempt interest income	**17**		
	18 Other tax-exempt income	**18**		
	19 Nondeductible expenses	**19**		
	20 Total property distributions (including cash) other than dividends reported on line 22 below	**20**		
	21 Other items and amounts required to be reported separately to shareholders (*attach schedule*)			
	22 Total dividend distributions paid from accumulated earnings and profits	**22**		
	23 **Income (loss).** (Required only if Schedule M-1 must be completed.) Combine lines 1 through 6 in column (b). From the result, subtract the sum of lines 7 through 11a, 15g, and 16b	**23**		

Form **1120S** (2001)

Form 1120S (2001)

Schedule L	Balance Sheets per Books	Beginning of tax year		End of tax year	
		(a)	(b)	(c)	(d)
	Assets				
1	Cash				
2a	Trade notes and accounts receivable . .				
b	Less allowance for bad debts				
3	Inventories				
4	U.S. Government obligations				
5	Tax-exempt securities				
6	Other current assets (attach schedule) .				
7	Loans to shareholders				
8	Mortgage and real estate loans . .				
9	Other investments (attach schedule) . .				
10a	Buildings and other depreciable assets .				
b	Less accumulated depreciation . . .				
11a	Depletable assets				
b	Less accumulated depletion.				
12	Land (net of any amortization)				
13a	Intangible assets (amortizable only) . .				
b	Less accumulated amortization. . . .				
14	Other assets (attach schedule)				
15	Total assets				
	Liabilities and Shareholders' Equity				
16	Accounts payable				
17	Mortgages, notes, bonds payable in less than 1 year				
18	Other current liabilities (attach schedule) .				
19	Loans from shareholders.				
20	Mortgages, notes, bonds payable in 1 year or more				
21	Other liabilities (attach schedule) . . .				
22	Capital stock				
23	Additional paid-in capital.				
24	Retained earnings				
25	Adjustments to shareholders' equity (attach schedule)				
26	Less cost of treasury stock		( )		( )
27	Total liabilities and shareholders' equity . .				

Schedule M-1 Reconciliation of Income (Loss) per Books With Income (Loss) per Return (You are not required to complete this schedule if the total assets on line 15, column (d), of Schedule L are less than $25,000.)

1	Net income (loss) per books. . . .		5	Income recorded on books this year not included on Schedule K, lines 1 through 6 (itemize):	
2	Income included on Schedule K, lines 1 through 6, not recorded on books this year (itemize):		a	Tax-exempt interest $ ----------------	
	-------------------------------------			----------------------------------	
3	Expenses recorded on books this year not included on Schedule K, lines 1 through 11a, 15g, and 16b (itemize):		6	Deductions included on Schedule K, lines 1 through 11a, 15g, and 16b, not charged against book income this year (itemize):	
a	Depreciation $ ------------------------		a	Depreciation $ ----------------	
b	Travel and entertainment $ --------------			----------------------------------	
	-------------------------------------		7	Add lines 5 and 6.	
4	Add lines 1 through 3.		8	Income (loss) (Schedule K, line 23). Line 4 less line 7	

Schedule M-2 Analysis of Accumulated Adjustments Account, Other Adjustments Account, and Shareholders' Undistributed Taxable Income Previously Taxed (see page 27 of the instructions)

		(a) Accumulated adjustments account	(b) Other adjustments account	(c) Shareholders' undistributed taxable income previously taxed
1	Balance at beginning of tax year . . .			
2	Ordinary income from page 1, line 21. .			
3	Other additions.			
4	Loss from page 1, line 21	( )		
5	Other reductions	( )	( )	
6	Combine lines 1 through 5			
7	Distributions other than dividend distributions.			
8	Balance at end of tax year. Subtract line 7 from line 6			

Form **1120S** (2001)

SCHEDULE K-1
(Form 1120S)

Department of the Treasury
Internal Revenue Service

Shareholder's Share of Income, Credits, Deductions, etc.

▶ See separate instructions.

For calendar year 2001 or tax year

beginning _____ , 2001, and ending _____ , 20 ___

OMB No. 1545-0130

2001

Shareholder's identifying number ▶

Corporation's identifying number ▶

Shareholder's name, address, and ZIP code

Corporation's name, address, and ZIP code

A Shareholder's percentage of stock ownership for tax year (see instructions for Schedule K-1) . . . . ▶ _____ %

B Internal Revenue Service Center where corporation filed its return ▶ _____

C Tax shelter registration number (see instructions for Schedule K-1) . . . . ▶ _____

D Check applicable boxes: **(1)** ☐ Final K-1   **(2)** ☐ Amended K-1

	(a) Pro rata share items		(b) Amount	(c) Form 1040 filers enter the amount in column (b) on:
Income (Loss)	**1** Ordinary income (loss) from trade or business activities . . .	1		See page 4 of the Shareholder's Instructions for Schedule K-1 (Form 1120S).
	2 Net income (loss) from rental real estate activities	2		
	3 Net income (loss) from other rental activities	3		
	4 Portfolio income (loss):			
	a Interest	4a		Sch. B, Part I, line 1
	b Ordinary dividends	4b		Sch. B, Part II, line 5
	c Royalties	4c		Sch. E, Part I, line 4
	d Net short-term capital gain (loss).	4d		Sch. D, line 5, col. (f)
	e (1) Net long-term capital gain (loss).	4e(1)		Sch. D, line 12, col. (f)
	(2) 28% rate gain (loss)	4e(2)		Sch. D, line 12, col. (g)
	(3) Qualified 5-year gain	4e(3)		Line 4 of worksheet for Sch. D, line 29
	f Other portfolio income (loss) *(attach schedule)*	4f		*(Enter on applicable line of your return.)*
	5 Net section 1231 gain (loss) (other than due to casualty or theft)	5		See Shareholder's Instructions for Schedule K-1 (Form 1120S).
	6 Other income (loss) *(attach schedule)*	6		*(Enter on applicable line of your return.)*
Deductions	**7** Charitable contributions *(attach schedule)*	7		Sch. A, line 15 or 16
	8 Section 179 expense deduction	8		See page 6 of the Shareholder's Instructions for Schedule K-1 (Form 1120S).
	9 Deductions related to portfolio income (loss) *(attach schedule)* .	9		
	10 Other deductions *(attach schedule)*	10		
Investment Interest	**11a** Interest expense on investment debts	11a		Form 4952, line 1
	b (1) Investment income included on lines 4a, 4b, 4c, and 4f above	11b(1)		See Shareholder's Instructions for Schedule K-1 (Form 1120S)
	(2) Investment expenses included on line 9 above	11b(2)		
Credits	**12a** Credit for alcohol used as fuel	12a		Form 6478, line 10
	b Low-income housing credit:			
	(1) From section 42(j)(5) partnerships	12b(1)		Form 8586, line 5
	(2) Other than on line 12b(1)	12b(2)		
	c Qualified rehabilitation expenditures related to rental real estate activities	12c		See pages 6 and 7 of the Shareholder's Instructions for Schedule K-1 (Form 1120S).
	d Credits (other than credits shown on lines 12b and 12c) related to rental real estate activities	12d		
	e Credits related to other rental activities	12e		
	13 Other credits	13		

For Paperwork Reduction Act Notice, see the Instructions for Form 1120S.

Cat. No. 11520D

Schedule K-1 (Form 1120S) 2001

(a) Pro rata share items		(b) Amount	(c) Form 1040 filers enter the amount in column (b) on:
Adjustments and Tax Preference Items			
14a Depreciation adjustment on property placed in service after 1986	14a		See page 7 of the Shareholder's Instructions for Schedule K-1 (Form 1120S) and Instructions for Form 6251
b Adjusted gain or loss	14b		
c Depletion (other than oil and gas)	14c		
d (1) Gross income from oil, gas, or geothermal properties . . .	14d(1)		
(2) Deductions allocable to oil, gas, or geothermal properties	14d(2)		
e Other adjustments and tax preference items (attach schedule) .	14e		
Foreign Taxes			
15a Name of foreign country or U.S. possession ▶			
b Gross income from all sources	15b		
c Gross income sourced at shareholder level	15c		
d Foreign gross income sourced at corporate level:			
(1) Passive	15d(1)		
(2) Listed categories (attach schedule)	15d(2)		
(3) General limitation	15d(3)		Form 1116, Part I
e Deductions allocated and apportioned at shareholder level:			
(1) Interest expense	15e(1)		
(2) Other	15e(2)		
f Deductions allocated and apportioned at corporate level to foreign source income:			
(1) Passive	15f(1)		
(2) Listed categories (attach schedule)	15f(2)		
(3) General limitation	15f(3)		
g Total foreign taxes (check one): ▶ ☐ Paid ☐ Accrued . .	15g		Form 1116, Part II
h Reduction in taxes available for credit (attach schedule) . . .	15h		See Instructions for Form 1116
Other			
16 Section 59(e)(2) expenditures: **a** Type ▶			See Shareholder's Instructions for Schedule K-1 (Form 1120S).
b Amount	16b		
17 Tax-exempt interest income	17		Form 1040, line 8b
18 Other tax-exempt income	18		See page 7 of the Shareholder's Instructions for Schedule K-1 (Form 1120S).
19 Nondeductible expenses	19		
20 Property distributions (including cash) other than dividend distributions reported to you on Form 1099-DIV	20		
21 Amount of loan repayments for "Loans From Shareholders" . .	21		
22 Recapture of low-income housing credit:			
a From section 42(j)(5) partnerships	22a		Form 8611, line 8
b Other than on line 22a	22b		

Supplemental Information

23 Supplemental information required to be reported separately to each shareholder (attach additional schedules if more space is needed):

....

....

....

....

....

....

....

....

....

....

Form **1040-ES**

Department of the Treasury
Internal Revenue Service

Estimated Tax for Individuals

This package is primarily for first-time filers of estimated tax.

OMB No. 1545-0087

2002

Purpose of This Package

Use this package to figure and pay your estimated tax. Estimated tax is the method used to pay tax on income that is not subject to withholding (for example, earnings from self-employment, interest, dividends, rents, alimony, etc.). In addition, if you do not elect voluntary withholding, you should make estimated tax payments on unemployment compensation and the taxable part of your social security benefits. See the 2001 instructions for your tax return for details on income that is taxable.

This package is primarily for first-time filers who are or may be subject to paying estimated tax. This package can also be used if you did not receive or have lost your preprinted 1040-ES package. The estimated tax worksheet on page 4 will help you figure the correct amount to pay. The payment vouchers in this package are for crediting your estimated tax payments to your account correctly if you are paying by check or money order. You may also be able to pay by Electronic Federal Tax Payment System (EFTPS), electronic funds withdrawal (direct debit), or credit card. See pages 4 and 5 for details. Use the **Record of Estimated Tax Payments** on page 6 to keep track of the payments you have made and the number and amount of your remaining payments.

After we receive your first payment voucher from this package (or if you make your first payment by EFTPS, electronic funds withdrawal, or credit card), we will mail you a 1040-ES package with your name, address, and social security number (SSN) preprinted on each payment voucher. Use the preprinted vouchers to make your **remaining** estimated tax payments for the year if you are paying by check or money order. This will speed processing, reduce processing costs, and reduce the chance of errors.

Do not use the vouchers in this package to notify the IRS of a **change of address.** If you have a new address, file **Form 8822,** Change of Address. The IRS will update your record and send you new preprinted payment vouchers.

Who Must Make Estimated Tax Payments

In most cases, you must make estimated tax payments if you expect to owe at least $1,000 in tax for 2002 (after subtracting your withholding and credits) and you expect your withholding and credits to be less than the **smaller** of:

1. 90% of the tax shown on your 2002 tax return **or**

2. The tax shown on your 2001 tax return (112% of that amount if you are not a farmer or fisherman and the adjusted gross income shown on that return is more than $150,000 or, if married filing separately for 2002, more than $75,000).

However, if you did not file a 2001 tax return or that return did not cover 12 months, item **2** above does not apply.

For this purpose, include household employment taxes (before subtracting advance EIC payments made to your employee(s)) when figuring the tax shown on your tax return if:

● You will have Federal income tax withheld from wages, pensions, annuities, gambling winnings, or other income **or**

● You would be required to make estimated tax payments to avoid a penalty even if you did not include household employment taxes when figuring your estimated tax.

Exception. You do not have to pay estimated tax if you were a U.S. citizen or resident alien for all of 2001 and you had no tax liability for the full 12-month 2001 tax year.

The estimated tax rules apply to:

● U.S. citizens and residents,

● Residents of Puerto Rico, the Virgin Islands, Guam, the Commonwealth of the Northern Mariana Islands, and American Samoa, and

● Nonresident aliens (use Form 1040-ES (NR)).

If you also receive salaries and wages, you may be able to avoid having to make estimated tax payments on your other income by asking your employer to take more tax out of your earnings. To do this, file a new **Form W-4,** Employee's Withholding Allowance Certificate, with your employer.

You can also choose to have Federal income tax withheld on certain government payments. For details, see **Form W-4V,** Voluntary Withholding Request.

Caution: *You may not make joint estimated tax payments if you or your spouse is a nonresident alien, you are separated under a decree of divorce or separate maintenance, or you and your spouse have different tax years.*

Additional Information You May Need

Most of the information you will need can be found in **Pub. 505,** Tax Withholding and Estimated Tax.

Other available information:

● **Pub. 553,** Highlights of 2001 Tax Changes.

● Instructions for the 2001 Form 1040 or 1040A.

● **What's Hot** at www.irs.gov.

For details on how to get forms and publications, see page 7 of the instructions for Form 1040 or 1040A.

If you have tax questions, call 1-800-829-1040 for assistance.

Changes Effective for 2002

Use your 2001 tax return as a guide in figuring your 2002 estimated tax, but be sure to consider the changes noted in this section. For more information on the changes below and other changes that may affect your 2002 estimated tax, see Pub. 553.

Reduced Tax Rates. Most of the tax rates have decreased by ½%, a new 10% tax rate applies to all filers, and the rate bracket amounts have increased. See the **2002 Tax Rate Schedules** on page 2. The rate reduction credit no longer applies.

Credit for Qualified Retirement Savings Contributions. You may be able to claim a credit of up to $1,000 for qualified retirement savings contributions (for example, contributions to an IRA or 401(k) plan) if your modified AGI is $50,000 or less.

Credit for Pension Plan Startup Costs. A general business credit of 50% of the qualified pension plan startup costs of an eligible employer may be allowed. The maximum credit is $500. An eligible employer is generally one who had 100 or fewer employees in the preceding tax year. See section 45E for more details.

Credit for Employer-Provided Child Care Costs. A general business credit of 25% of the qualified child care facility costs plus 10% of the qualified child care resource and referral costs may be allowed. The maximum credit is $150,000. See section 45F for more details.

Adoption Credit. The maximum adoption credit has increased to $10,000 per adopted child. The credit is allowed only if your modified AGI is less than $190,000.

Certain Credits No Longer Reduce Alternative Minimum Tax (AMT). The credit for child and dependent care expenses, credit for the elderly or the disabled, education credits, mortgage interest credit, and District of Columbia first-time homebuyer credit no longer reduce AMT. However, the child tax credit, adoption credit, and the credit for qualified retirement savings contributions may reduce your AMT.

Student Loan Interest Deduction. The 60-month limit no longer applies. But you cannot take the deduction if your modified AGI is $65,000 or more ($130,000 or more if married filing jointly).

Deduction for Qualified Higher Education Expenses. You may be able to deduct up to $3,000 of qualified higher education expenses paid for yourself, your spouse, or your dependents. But you cannot take the deduction if your modified AGI is more than $65,000 ($130,000 if married filing jointly). Also, you cannot claim both the deduction for qualified higher education expenses and a Hope or lifetime learning credit for the same student.

Cat. No. 11340T

Traditional IRA Deduction Increased. You, and your spouse if filing jointly, each may be able to deduct up to $3,000 ($3,500 if age 50 or older at the end of 2002). If you are covered by a retirement plan, your modified AGI must be less than $44,000 (less than $64,000 if married filing jointly or qualifying widow(er)) to take a deduction.

Self-Employed Health Insurance Deduction. You may be able to deduct up to 70% of your health insurance expenses.

Estimated Tax Safe Harbor for Some Taxpayers. The estimated tax safe harbor that is based on the tax shown on your 2001 tax return is 112% of that amount if you are not a farmer or fisherman and the AGI shown on that return is more than $150,000 or, if married filing separately for 2002, $75,000.

Standard Mileage Rate. The rate for business use of a vehicle has increased to 36.5 cents a mile. The rate for use of your vehicle to obtain medical care or for deductible moving expenses has increased to 13 cents a mile.

Foreign Earned Income Exclusion. The maximum foreign earned income exclusion amount is $80,000.

Disaster Relief Payments. Qualified disaster relief payments are excluded from gross income and net earnings from self-employment. Generally, such payments include the following amounts received as a result of a qualified disaster.

- Payments to cover personal, family, living, or funeral expenses.
- Payments for the repair or rehabilitation of a personal residence.
- Payments from common carriers made because of the physical injuries or death of an individual.
- Disaster payments received from a Federal, state, or local government or agency.

However, this exclusion does not apply to the extent any expense compensated by such payments was also compensated for by insurance or otherwise. For more details, see section 139.

Disability Income Exclusion. Gross income does not include amounts received as disability income attributable to injuries incurred as a direct result of any:

- Terrorist activity directed against the United States or any of its allies or
- Military action involving the U.S. Armed Forces and resulting from violence or aggression against the United States or any of its allies.

Standard Deduction. If you do not itemize your deductions, you may take the 2002 standard deduction listed below for your filing status.

Filing Status	Standard Deduction
Married filing jointly or Qualifying widow(er)	$7,850
Head of household	$6,900
Single	$4,700
Married filing separately	$3,925

However, if you can be claimed as a dependent on another person's 2002 return, your standard deduction is the **greater** of:

- **$750** or
- Your earned income plus $250 (up to the standard deduction amount).

Your standard deduction is increased by the following amount if:

1. You are an unmarried individual (single or head of household) and are:

65 or older or blind	$1,150
65 or older and blind	$2,300

2. You are a married individual (filing jointly or separately) or a qualifying widow(er) and are:

65 or older or blind	$900
65 or older and blind	$1,800
Both spouses 65 or older	$1,800 *
Both spouses 65 or older and blind	$3,600 *

* If married filing separately, these amounts apply only if you can claim an exemption for your spouse.

To Figure Your Estimated Tax, Use:

- The **2002 Estimated Tax Worksheet** on page 4.
- The instructions for the worksheet on page 4 that begin on page 3.
- The **2002 Tax Rate Schedules** below.
- Your 2001 tax return and instructions, as a guide to figuring your income, deductions, and credits (but be sure to consider the changes noted earlier).

If you receive your income unevenly throughout the year (for example, because you operate your business on a seasonal basis), you may be able to lower or eliminate the amount of your required estimated tax payment for one or more periods by using the annualized income installment method. See Pub. 505 for details.

2002 Tax Rate Schedules

Caution: *Do not use these Tax Rate Schedules to figure your 2001 taxes. Use only to figure your 2002 estimated taxes.*

Single—Schedule X

If line 5 is: Over-	But not over-	The tax is:	of the amount over-
$0	$ 6,000	----------- 10%	$0
6,000	27,950	$600.00 + 15%	6,000
27,950	67,700	3,892.50 + 27%	27,950
67,700	141,250	14,625.00 + 30%	67,700
141,250	307,050	36,690.00 + 35%	141,250
307,050	----------	94,720.00 + 38.6%	307,050

Head of household—Schedule Z

If line 5 is: Over-	But not over-	The tax is:	of the amount over-
$0	$10,000	----------- 10%	$0
10,000	37,450	$1,000.00 + 15%	10,000
37,450	96,700	5,117.50 + 27%	37,450
96,700	156,600	21,115.00 + 30%	96,700
156,600	307,050	39,085.00 + 35%	156,600
307,050	----------	91,742.50 + 38.6%	307,050

Married filing jointly or Qualifying widow(er)—Schedule Y-1

If line 5 is: Over-	But not over-	The tax is:	of the amount over-
$0	$12,000	----------- 10%	$0
12,000	46,700	$1,200.00 + 15%	12,000
46,700	112,850	6,405.00 + 27%	46,700
112,850	171,950	24,265.50 + 30%	112,850
171,950	307,050	41,995.50 + 35%	171,950
307,050	----------	89,280.50 + 38.6%	307,050

Married filing separately—Schedule Y-2

If line 5 is: Over-	But not over-	The tax is:	of the amount over-
$0	$ 6,000	----------- 10%	$0
6,000	23,350	$600.00 + 15%	6,000
23,350	56,425	3,202.50 + 27%	23,350
56,425	85,975	12,132.75 + 30%	56,425
85,975	153,525	20,997.75 + 35%	85,975
153,525	----------	44,640.25 + 38.6%	153,525

To amend or correct your estimated tax, see **Amending Estimated Tax Payments** below.

Instructions for Worksheet on Page 4

Line 1. Adjusted Gross Income. Use your 2001 tax return and instructions as a guide to figuring the adjusted gross income you expect in 2002 (but be sure to consider the changes noted earlier). For more details on figuring your adjusted gross income, see **Expected Adjusted Gross Income** in Pub. 505. If you are self-employed, be sure to take into account the deduction for one-half of your self-employment tax.

Line 8. Include on this line the additional taxes from **Form 4972,** Tax on Lump-Sum Distributions, or **Form 8814,** Parents' Election To Report Child's Interest and Dividends. Also include any recapture of the education credits.

Line 9. Credits. See the 2001 Form 1040, lines 43 through 50, or Form 1040A, lines 27 through 32, and the related instructions. However, be sure to see **Certain Credits No Longer Reduce Alternative Minimum Tax (AMT)** on page 1.

Line 11. Self-Employment Tax. If you and your spouse make joint estimated tax payments and you both have self-employment income, figure the self-employment tax for each of you separately. Enter the total on line 11. When figuring your estimate of 2002 net earnings from self-employment, be sure to use only 92.35% of your total net profit from self-employment.

Line 12. Other Taxes. Except as noted below, enter any other taxes, such as the taxes on accumulation distribution of trusts, distributions from an Archer MSA or Coverdell education savings account, and early distributions from **(a)** an IRA or other qualified retirement plan, **(b)** an annuity, or **(c)** a modified endowment contract entered into after June 20, 1988.

Include household employment taxes (before subtracting advance EIC payments made to your employee(s)) on line 12 if:
- You will have Federal income tax withheld from wages, pensions, annuities, gambling winnings, or other income **or**
- You would be required to make estimated tax payments (to avoid a penalty) even if you did not include household employment taxes when figuring your estimated tax.

Do not include tax on recapture of a Federal mortgage subsidy, social security and Medicare tax on unreported tip income, and uncollected employee social security and Medicare or RRTA tax on tips or group-term life insurance. These taxes are not required to be paid until the due date of your income tax return (not including extensions).

Line 17. If you are a household employer and you make advance EIC payments to your employee(s), reduce your required payment for each period by the amount of advance EIC payments paid during the period.

Payment Due Dates

You may pay all of your estimated tax by April 15, 2002, or in four equal amounts by the dates shown below.

1st payment	April 15, 2002
2nd payment	June 17, 2002
3rd payment	Sept. 16, 2002
4th payment	Jan. 15, 2003*

*You do not have to make the payment due January 15, 2003, if you file your 2002 tax return by January 31, 2003, **and** pay the entire balance due with your return.

Note: *Payments are due by the dates indicated whether or not you are outside the United States and Puerto Rico.*

If, after March 31, 2002, you have a large change in income, deductions, additional taxes, or credits that requires you to start making estimated tax payments, you should figure the amount of your estimated tax payments by using the annualized income installment method, explained in Pub. 505. Although your payment due dates will be the same as shown above, the payment amounts will vary based on your income, deductions, additional taxes, and credits for the months ending before each payment due date. As a result, this method may allow you to skip or lower the amount due for one or more payments. If you use the annualized income installment method, be sure to file **Form 2210,** Underpayment of Estimated Tax by Individuals, Estates, and Trusts, with your 2002 tax return, even if no penalty is owed.

Farmers and fishermen. If at least two-thirds of your gross income for 2001 or 2002 is from farming or fishing, you may do one of the following.
- Pay all of your estimated tax by January 15, 2003.
- File your 2002 Form 1040 by March 3, 2003, and pay the total tax due. In this case, 2002 estimated payments are not required to avoid a penalty.

Fiscal year taxpayers. You are on a fiscal year if your 12-month tax period ends on any day except December 31. Due dates for fiscal year taxpayers are the 15th day of the 4th, 6th, and 9th months of your current fiscal year and the 1st month of the following fiscal year. If any payment date falls on a Saturday, Sunday, or legal holiday, use the next business day.

Name Change

If you changed your name and made estimated tax payments using your old name, attach a statement to the front of your 2002 tax return. List all of the estimated tax payments you and your spouse made for 2002 and the name(s) and SSN(s) under which you made the payments.

Amending Estimated Tax Payments

To change or amend your estimated tax payments, refigure your total estimated tax payments due (line 16 of the worksheet on page 4). Then, use the worksheets under **Amended estimated tax** in Chapter 2 of Pub. 505 to figure the payment due for each remaining payment period. If an estimated tax payment for a previous period is less than ¼ of your amended estimated tax, you may owe a penalty when you file your return.

When a Penalty Is Applied

In some cases, you may owe a penalty when you file your return. The penalty is imposed on each underpayment for the number of days it remains unpaid. A penalty may be applied if you did not pay enough estimated tax for the year or you did not make the payments on time or in the required amount. A penalty may apply even if you have an overpayment on your tax return.

The penalty may be waived under certain conditions. See Pub. 505 for details.

Paying by Check or Money Order Using the Payment Voucher

There is a separate payment voucher for each due date. The due date is shown in the upper right corner. Please be sure you use the voucher with the correct due date for each payment you make. Complete and send in the voucher **only** if you are making a payment by check or money order. To complete the voucher, do the following.

- Type or print your name, address, and SSN in the space provided on the voucher. If filing a joint voucher, also enter your spouse's name and SSN. List the names and SSNs in the same order on the joint voucher as you will list them on your joint return. If you and your spouse plan to file separate returns, file separate vouchers instead of a joint voucher.

- Enter in the payment box of the voucher only the amount you are sending in by check or money order. When making payments of estimated tax, be sure to take into account any 2001 overpayment that you choose to credit against your 2002 tax, but **do not** include the overpayment amount in the payment box.

- Make your check or money order payable to the "**United States Treasury.**" Do not send cash. To help us process your payment, enter the amount on the right side of the check like this: $ XXX.XX. Do not use dashes or lines (for example, do not enter "$ XXX-" or "$ XXX $\frac{XX}{100}$").

- Write "2002 Form 1040-ES" and your SSN on your check or money order. If you are filing a joint voucher, enter the SSN that you will show first on your joint tax return.

- Enclose, but do not staple or attach, your payment with the voucher.

- Mail your payment voucher and check or money order to the address shown on page 6 for the place where you live.
- Fill in the **Record of Estimated Tax Payments** on page 6 for your files.

Paying by Electronic Federal Tax Payment System (EFTPS)

You can use EFTPS to submit your estimated payment electronically using the Internet, personal computer software, or phone. You can schedule payments for withdrawal up to 365 days in advance. You can make payments weekly, monthly, or quarterly. For more information, call 1-800-555-4477 or 1-800-945-8400, or visit the EFTPS Web Site at www.eftps.gov.

Paying by Electronic Funds Withdrawal

You may make one 2002 estimated tax payment when you electronically file your 2001 tax return by authorizing an electronic funds withdrawal (direct debit) from your checking or savings account. You will need to know your account number and your financial institution's routing number. You can check with your financial institution to make sure that an electronic withdrawal is allowed and to get the correct routing and account numbers. Whether or not you have a balance due on your electronically filed tax return, you can schedule one estimated tax payment with an effective date of April 15, 2002, June 17, 2002, or September 16, 2002. Check with your tax return preparer or tax preparation software for details. **Do not** send in a Form 1040-ES payment voucher when you schedule an estimated tax payment by electronic funds withdrawal.

2002 Estimated Tax Worksheet (keep for your records)

1	Enter amount of adjusted gross income you expect in 2002 (see instructions)	**1**
2	• If you plan to itemize deductions, enter the estimated total of your itemized deductions. **Caution:** *If line 1 above is over $137,300 ($68,650 if married filing separately), your deduction may be reduced. See Pub. 505 for details.* • If you do not plan to itemize deductions, see **Standard Deduction** on page 2 and enter your standard deduction here.	**2**
3	Subtract line 2 from line 1	**3**
4	Exemptions. Multiply $3,000 by the number of personal exemptions. If you can be claimed as a dependent on another person's 2002 return, your personal exemption is not allowed. **Caution:** *See Pub. 505 to figure the amount to enter if line 1 above is over: $206,000 if married filing jointly or qualifying widow(er); $171,650 if head of household; $137,300 if single; or $103,000 if married filing separately*	**4**
5	Subtract line 4 from line 3	**5**
6	**Tax.** Figure your tax on the amount on line 5 by using the **2002 Tax Rate Schedules** on page 2. **Caution:** *If you have a net capital gain, see Pub. 505 to figure the tax*	**6**
7	Alternative minimum tax from Form 6251	**7**
8	Add lines 6 and 7. Also include any tax from Forms 4972 and 8814 and any recapture of the education credits (see instructions)	**8**
9	Credits (see instructions). **Do not** include any income tax withholding on this line	**9**
10	Subtract line 9 from line 8. If zero or less, enter -0-	**10**
11	Self-employment tax (see instructions). Estimate of 2002 net earnings from self-employment $_____ ; if **$84,900 or less,** multiply the amount by 15.3%; if **more than $84,900,** multiply the amount by 2.9%, add $10,527.60 to the result, and enter the total. **Caution:** *If you also have wages subject to social security tax, see Pub. 505 to figure the amount to enter* . .	**11**
12	Other taxes (see instructions)	**12**
13a	Add lines 10 through 12	**13a**
b	Earned income credit, additional child tax credit, and credit from **Form 4136**	**13b**
c	**Total 2002 estimated tax.** Subtract line 13b from line 13a. If zero or less, enter -0- . . . ▶	**13c**
14a	Multiply line 13c by 90% (66⅔% for farmers and fishermen) . . .	**14a**
b	Enter the tax shown on your 2001 tax return (112% of that amount if you are not a farmer or fisherman and the adjusted gross income shown on line 34 of that return is more than $150,000 or, if married filing separately for 2002, more than $75,000)	**14b**
c	**Required annual payment to avoid a penalty.** Enter the **smaller** of line 14a or 14b . . . ▶	**14c**
	Caution: *Generally, if you do not prepay (through income tax withholding and estimated tax payments) at least the amount on line 14c, you may owe a penalty for not paying enough estimated tax. To avoid a penalty, make sure your estimate on line 13c is as accurate as possible. Even if you pay the required annual payment, you may still owe tax when you file your return. If you prefer, you may pay the amount shown on line 13c. For details, see Pub. 505.*	
15	Income tax withheld and estimated to be withheld during 2002 (including income tax withholding on pensions, annuities, certain deferred income, etc.)	**15**
16	Subtract line 15 from line 14c. **(Note:** *If zero or less or line 13c minus line 15 is less than $1,000, stop here. You are not required to make estimated tax payments.)*	**16**
17	If the first payment you are required to make is due April 15, 2002, enter ¼ of line 16 (minus any 2001 overpayment that you are applying to this installment) here, and on your payment voucher(s) if you are paying by check or money order. **(Note:** *Household employers, see instructions.)* . .	**17**

Page 4

Paying by Credit Card

You may use your American Express' Card, Discover' Card, or MasterCard' card to make estimated tax payments. Call toll free or access by Internet one of the service providers listed below and follow the instructions of the provider. Each provider will charge a convenience fee based on the amount you are paying. Fees may vary between providers. You will be told what the fee is during the transaction and you will have the option to either continue or cancel the transaction. You can also find out what the fee will be by calling the provider's toll-free automated customer service number or visiting the provider's Web Site shown below.

PhoneCharge, Inc.
1-888-ALLTAXX (1-888-255-8299)
1-877-851-9964 (Customer Service)
www.1888ALLTAXX.com

Official Payments Corporation
1-800-2PAY-TAX (1-800-272-9829)
1-877-754-4413 (Customer Service)
www.officialpayments.com

If you complete the payment, you will be given a confirmation number at the end of the call. Fill in the **Record of Estimated Tax Payments** on page 6. Enter the confirmation number in column **(b)**, but **do not** include the amount of the convenience fee in column **(c)**. There is nothing to send in when you pay by credit card.

Privacy Act and Paperwork Reduction Act Notice. The Privacy Act of 1974 and the Paperwork Reduction Act of 1980 require that when we ask you for information we must first tell you our legal right to ask for the information, why we are asking for it, and how it will be used. We must also tell you what could happen if we do not receive it and whether your response is voluntary, required to obtain a benefit, or mandatory under the law.

This notice applies to all papers you file with us. It also applies to any questions we need to ask you so we can complete, correct, or process your return; figure your tax; and collect tax, interest, or penalties.

Our legal right to ask for information is Internal Revenue Code sections 6001, 6011, and 6012(a), and their regulations. They say that you must file a return or statement with us for any tax for which you are liable. Your response is mandatory under these sections. Code section 6109 and its regulations say that you must provide your taxpayer identification number on what you file. This is so we know who you are, and can process your return and other papers.

You are not required to provide the information requested on a form that is subject to the Paperwork Reduction Act unless the form displays a valid OMB control number. Books or records relating to a form or its instructions must be retained as long as their contents may become material in the administration of any Internal Revenue law. Generally, tax returns and return information are confidential, as stated in Code section 6103.

We ask for tax return information to carry out the tax laws of the United States. We need it to figure and collect the right amount of tax.

We may give the information to the Department of Justice and to other Federal agencies, as provided by law. We may also give it to cities, states, the District of Columbia, and U.S. commonwealths or possessions to carry out their tax laws. And we may give it to foreign governments because of tax treaties they have with the United States.

If you do not file a return, do not give the information asked for, or give fraudulent information, you may be charged penalties and be subject to criminal prosecution.

Please keep this notice with your records. It may help you if we ask you for other information. If you have any questions about the rules for filing and giving information, please call or visit any Internal Revenue Service office.

The time needed to complete the worksheets and prepare and file the payment vouchers will vary depending on individual circumstances. The estimated average time is: **Recordkeeping,** 52 min.; **Learning about the law,** 28 min.; **Preparing the worksheets and payment vouchers,** 48 min.; **Copying, assembling, and sending the payment voucher to the IRS,** 10 min. If you have comments concerning the accuracy of these time estimates or suggestions for making this package simpler, we would be happy to hear from you. You can write to the Tax Forms Committee, Western Area Distribution Center, Rancho Cordova, CA 95743-0001. **Do not** send the payment vouchers to this address. Instead, see **Where To File Your Payment Voucher if Paying by Check or Money Order** on page 6.

Record of Estimated Tax Payments (Farmers, fishermen, and fiscal year taxpayers, see page 3 for payment due dates.)

Payment number	Payment due date	(a) Date paid	(b) Check or money order number or credit card confirmation number	(c) Amount paid (do not include any credit card convenience fee)	(d) 2001 overpayment credit applied	(e) Total amount paid and credited (add (c) and (d))
1	4/15/2002					
2	6/17/2002					
3	9/16/2002					
4	1/15/2003*					
Total . . . . ▶						

*You do not have to make this payment if you file your 2002 tax return by January 31, 2003, **and** pay the entire balance due with your return.

Where To File Your Payment Voucher if Paying by Check or Money Order

Mail your payment voucher and check or money order to the Internal Revenue Service at the address shown below for the place where you live. **Do not** mail your tax return to this address **or** send an estimated tax payment without a payment voucher. Also, do not mail your estimated tax payments to the address shown in the Form 1040 or 1040A instructions. If you need more payment vouchers, use another Form 1040-ES package.

Note: For proper delivery of your estimated tax payment to a P.O. box, you must include the box number in the address. Also, note that only the U.S. Postal Service can deliver to P.O. boxes.

IF you live in . . .   ▼

THEN use . . .   ▼

Connecticut, Delaware, New Jersey, New York (New York City and counties of Nassau, Rockland, Suffolk, and Westchester)	P.O. Box 162 Newark, NJ 07101-0162
New York (all other counties), Maine, Massachusetts, Michigan, New Hampshire, Rhode Island, Vermont	P.O. Box 7350 Philadelphia, PA 19101-7350

District of Columbia, Indiana, Maryland, Ohio, Pennsylvania	P.O. Box 80102 Cincinnati, OH 45280-0002
Florida, Georgia, North Carolina, South Carolina, West Virginia	P.O. Box 105900 Atlanta, GA 30348-5900
Alabama, Arkansas, Kentucky, Louisiana, Mississippi, Oklahoma, Tennessee, Virginia	P.O. Box 105225 Atlanta, GA 30348-5225
Illinois, Iowa, Kansas, Minnesota, Missouri, Oregon, Wisconsin	P.O. Box 970006 St. Louis, MO 63197-0006
Arizona, Colorado, Idaho, Montana, New Mexico, Texas, Utah, Wyoming	P.O. Box 660406 Dallas, TX 75266-0406
Alaska, California, Hawaii, Nevada	P.O. Box 510000 San Francisco, CA 94151-5100
Nebraska, North Dakota, South Dakota, Washington	P.O. Box 54919 Los Angeles, CA 90054-0919

All APO and FPO addresses, American Samoa, the Commonwealth of the Northern Mariana Islands, nonpermanent residents of Guam or the Virgin Islands, Puerto Rico (or if excluding income under section 933), or a foreign country (U.S. citizens and those filing Form 2555, Form 2555-EZ, or Form 4563)	P.O. Box 80102 Cincinnati, OH 45280-0002
Permanent residents of Guam*	Department of Revenue and Taxation Government of Guam P.O. Box 23607 GMF, GU 96921
Permanent residents of the Virgin Islands*	V.I. Bureau of Internal Revenue 9601 Estate Thomas Charlotte Amalie St. Thomas, VI 00802

* Permanent residents must prepare separate vouchers for estimated income tax and self-employment tax payments. Send the income tax vouchers to the address for permanent residents and the self-employment tax vouchers to the address for nonpermanent residents.

- - - - - - - - - - - - - - - - Tear off here - - - - - - - - - - - - - - - -

Form **1040-ES**
Department of the Treasury
Internal Revenue Service

2002 Payment Voucher **4**

OMB No. 1545-0087

File only if you are making a payment of estimated tax by check or money order. Mail this voucher with your check or money order payable to the **"United States Treasury."** Write your social security number and "2002 Form 1040-ES" on your check or money order. Do not send cash. Enclose, but do not staple or attach, your payment with this voucher.

Calendar year—Due Jan. 15, 2003

Amount of estimated tax you are paying by check or money order.

Dollars	Cents

Type or print

Your first name and initial	Your last name	Your social security number

If joint payment, complete for spouse

Spouse's first name and initial	Spouse's last name	Spouse's social security number

Address (number, street, and apt. no.)

City, state, and ZIP code (If a foreign address, enter city, province or state, postal code, and country.)

For Privacy Act and Paperwork Reduction Act Notice, see instructions on page 5.

2002 Payment Voucher **3**

OMB No. 1545-0087

File only if you are making a payment of estimated tax by check or money order. Mail this voucher with your check or money order payable to the **"United States Treasury."** Write your social security number and "2002 Form 1040-ES" on your check or money order. Do not send cash. Enclose, but do not staple or attach, your payment with this voucher.

Calendar year—Due Sept. 16, 2002

Amount of estimated tax you are paying by check or money order.

Dollars	Cents

Type or print	Your first name and initial	Your last name	Your social security number
	If joint payment, complete for spouse		
	Spouse's first name and initial	Spouse's last name	Spouse's social security number
	Address (number, street, and apt. no.)		
	City, state, and ZIP code (If a foreign address, enter city, province or state, postal code, and country.)		

For Privacy Act and Paperwork Reduction Act Notice, see instructions on page 5.

- Tear off here -

2002 Payment Voucher **2**

OMB No. 1545-0087

File only if you are making a payment of estimated tax by check or money order. Mail this voucher with your check or money order payable to the **"United States Treasury."** Write your social security number and "2002 Form 1040-ES" on your check or money order. Do not send cash. Enclose, but do not staple or attach, your payment with this voucher.

Calendar year—Due June 17, 2002

Amount of estimated tax you are paying by check or money order.

Dollars	Cents

Type or print	Your first name and initial	Your last name	Your social security number
	If joint payment, complete for spouse		
	Spouse's first name and initial	Spouse's last name	Spouse's social security number
	Address (number, street, and apt. no.)		
	City, state, and ZIP code (If a foreign address, enter city, province or state, postal code, and country.)		

For Privacy Act and Paperwork Reduction Act Notice, see instructions on page 5.

- Tear off here -

2002 Payment Voucher **1**

OMB No. 1545-0087

File only if you are making a payment of estimated tax by check or money order. Mail this voucher with your check or money order payable to the **"United States Treasury."** Write your social security number and "2002 Form 1040-ES" on your check or money order. Do not send cash. Enclose, but do not staple or attach, your payment with this voucher.

Calendar year—Due April 15, 2002

Amount of estimated tax you are paying by check or money order.

Dollars	Cents

Type or print	Your first name and initial	Your last name	Your social security number
	If joint payment, complete for spouse		
	Spouse's first name and initial	Spouse's last name	Spouse's social security number
	Address (number, street, and apt. no.)		
	City, state, and ZIP code (If a foreign address, enter city, province or state, postal code, and country.)		

For Privacy Act and Paperwork Reduction Act Notice, see instructions on page 5.

Form **8829**	**Expenses for Business Use of Your Home**	OMB No. 1545-1266
	▶ File only with Schedule C (Form 1040). Use a separate Form 8829 for each home you used for business during the year.	**2001**
Department of the Treasury Internal Revenue Service (99)	▶ See separate instructions.	Attachment Sequence No. **66**

Name(s) of proprietor(s)

Your social security number

Part I   Part of Your Home Used for Business

1	Area used regularly and exclusively for business, regularly for day care, or for storage of inventory or product samples. See instructions	**1**	
2	Total area of home	**2**	
3	Divide line 1 by line 2. Enter the result as a percentage	**3**	%
	• **For day-care facilities not used exclusively for business, also complete lines 4-6.**		
	• **All others, skip lines 4-6 and enter the amount from line 3 on line 7.**		
4	Multiply days used for day care during year by hours used per day	**4**	hr.
5	Total hours available for use during the year (365 days × 24 hours). See instructions	**5**	8,760 hr.
6	Divide line 4 by line 5. Enter the result as a decimal amount	**6**	.
7	Business percentage. For day-care facilities not used exclusively for business, multiply line 6 by line 3 (enter the result as a percentage). All others, enter the amount from line 3 ▶	**7**	%

Part II   Figure Your Allowable Deduction

8	Enter the amount from Schedule C, line 29, **plus** any net gain or (loss) derived from the business use of your home and shown on Schedule D or Form 4797. If more than one place of business, see instructions		**8**	

	See instructions for columns (a) and (b) before completing lines 9-20.		(a) Direct expenses	(b) Indirect expenses		
9	Casualty losses. See instructions	**9**				
10	Deductible mortgage interest. See instructions	**10**				
11	Real estate taxes. See instructions	**11**				
12	Add lines 9, 10, and 11	**12**				
13	Multiply line 12, column (b) by line 7		**13**			
14	Add line 12, column (a) and line 13				**14**	
15	Subtract line 14 from line 8. If zero or less, enter -0-				**15**	
16	Excess mortgage interest. See instructions	**16**				
17	Insurance	**17**				
18	Repairs and maintenance	**18**				
19	Utilities	**19**				
20	Other expenses. See instructions	**20**				
21	Add lines 16 through 20	**21**				
22	Multiply line 21, column (b) by line 7		**22**			
23	Carryover of operating expenses from 2000 Form 8829, line 41		**23**			
24	Add line 21 in column (a), line 22, and line 23				**24**	
25	Allowable operating expenses. Enter the **smaller** of line 15 or line 24				**25**	
26	Limit on excess casualty losses and depreciation. Subtract line 25 from line 15				**26**	
27	Excess casualty losses. See instructions		**27**			
28	Depreciation of your home from Part III below		**28**			
29	Carryover of excess casualty losses and depreciation from 2000 Form 8829, line 42		**29**			
30	Add lines 27 through 29				**30**	
31	Allowable excess casualty losses and depreciation. Enter the **smaller** of line 26 or line 30				**31**	
32	Add lines 14, 25, and 31				**32**	
33	Casualty loss portion, if any, from lines 14 and 31. Carry amount to **Form 4684**, Section B				**33**	
34	Allowable expenses for business use of your home. Subtract line 33 from line 32. Enter here and on Schedule C, line 30. If your home was used for more than one business, see instructions ▶				**34**	

Part III   Depreciation of Your Home

35	Enter the **smaller** of your home's adjusted basis or its fair market value. See instructions	**35**	
36	Value of land included on line 35	**36**	
37	Basis of building. Subtract line 36 from line 35	**37**	
38	Business basis of building. Multiply line 37 by line 7	**38**	
39	Depreciation percentage. See instructions	**39**	%
40	Depreciation allowable. Multiply line 38 by line 39. Enter here and on line 28 above. See instructions	**40**	

Part IV   Carryover of Unallowed Expenses to 2002

41	Operating expenses. Subtract line 25 from line 24. If less than zero, enter -0-	**41**	
42	Excess casualty losses and depreciation. Subtract line 31 from line 30. If less than zero, enter -0-	**42**	

For Paperwork Reduction Act Notice, see page 4 of separate instructions.   Cat. No. 13232M   Form **8829** (2001)

Form **SS-4**

(Rev. December 2001)

Department of the Treasury
Internal Revenue Service

Application for Employer Identification Number

(For use by employers, corporations, partnerships, trusts, estates, churches, government agencies, Indian tribal entities, certain individuals, and others.)

▶ See separate instructions for each line.   ▶ Keep a copy for your records.

EIN

OMB No. 1545-0003

Type or print clearly.

1 Legal name of entity (or individual) for whom the EIN is being requested

2 Trade name of business (if different from name on line 1)

3 Executor, trustee, "care of" name

4a Mailing address (room, apt., suite no. and street, or P.O. box)

5a Street address (if different) (Do not enter a P.O. box.)

4b City, state, and ZIP code

5b City, state, and ZIP code

6 County and state where principal business is located

7a Name of principal officer, general partner, grantor, owner, or trustor

7b SSN, ITIN, or EIN

8a **Type of entity** (check only one box)

☐ Sole proprietor (SSN) _____
☐ Partnership
☐ Corporation (enter form number to be filed) ▶ _____
☐ Personal service corp.
☐ Church or church-controlled organization
☐ Other nonprofit organization (specify) ▶ _____
☐ Other (specify) ▶

☐ Estate (SSN of decedent) _____
☐ Plan administrator (SSN) _____
☐ Trust (SSN of grantor) _____
☐ National Guard   ☐ State/local government
☐ Farmers' cooperative   ☐ Federal government/military
☐ REMIC   ☐ Indian tribal governments/enterprises
Group Exemption Number (GEN) ▶ _____

8b If a corporation, name the state or foreign country (if applicable) where incorporated

State

Foreign country

9 **Reason for applying** (check only one box)

☐ Started new business (specify type) ▶ _____

☐ Hired employees (Check the box and see line 12.)
☐ Compliance with IRS withholding regulations
☐ Other (specify) ▶

☐ Banking purpose (specify purpose) ▶ _____
☐ Changed type of organization (specify new type) ▶ _____
☐ Purchased going business
☐ Created a trust (specify type) ▶ _____
☐ Created a pension plan (specify type) ▶ _____

10 Date business started or acquired (month, day, year)

11 Closing month of accounting year

12 First date wages or annuities were paid or will be paid (month, day, year). **Note:** *If applicant is a withholding agent, enter date income will first be paid to nonresident alien. (month, day, year)* . . . . ▶

13 Highest number of employees expected in the next 12 months. **Note:** *If the applicant does not expect to have any employees during the period, enter "-0-."* . . . . ▶

Agricultural	Household	Other

14 Check **one** box that best describes the principal activity of your business.

☐ Construction   ☐ Rental & leasing   ☐ Transportation & warehousing
☐ Real estate   ☐ Manufacturing   ☐ Finance & insurance

☐ Health care & social assistance   ☐ Wholesale–agent/broker
☐ Accommodation & food service   ☐ Wholesale–other   ☐ Retail
☐ Other (specify)

15 Indicate principal line of merchandise sold; specific construction work done; products produced; or services provided.

16a Has the applicant ever applied for an employer identification number for this or any other business? . . . . .   ☐ **Yes**   ☐ **No**
Note: *If "Yes," please complete lines 16b and 16c.*

16b If you checked "Yes" on line 16a, give applicant's legal name and trade name shown on prior application if different from line 1 or 2 above.
Legal name ▶   Trade name ▶

16c Approximate date when, and city and state where, the application was filed. Enter previous employer identification number if known.
Approximate date when filed (mo., day, year)   City and state where filed   Previous EIN

Third Party Designee	Complete this section **only** if you want to authorize the named individual to receive the entity's EIN and answer questions about the completion of this form.	
	Designee's name	Designee's telephone number (include area code) ( )
	Address and ZIP code	Designee's fax number (include area code) ( )

Under penalties of perjury, I declare that I have examined this application, and to the best of my knowledge and belief, it is true, correct, and complete.

Name and title (type or print clearly) ▶

Applicant's telephone number (include area code) ( )

Signature ▶   Date ▶

Applicant's fax number (include area code) ( )

For Privacy Act and Paperwork Reduction Act Notice, see separate instructions.   Cat. No. 16055N   Form **SS-4** (Rev. 12-2001)

Do I Need an EIN?

File Form SS-4 if the applicant entity does not already have an EIN but is required to show an EIN on any return, statement, or other document.[1] **See also the separate instructions for each line on Form SS-4.**

IF the applicant...	AND...	THEN...
Started a new business	Does not currently have (nor expect to have) employees	Complete lines 1, 2, 4a–6, 8a, and 9–16c.
Hired (or will hire) employees, including household employees	Does not already have an EIN	Complete lines 1, 2, 4a–6, 7a–b (if applicable), 8a, 8b (if applicable), and 9–16c.
Opened a bank account	Needs an EIN for banking purposes only	Complete lines 1–5b, 7a–b (if applicable), 8a, 9, and 16a–c.
Changed type of organization	Either the legal character of the organization or its ownership changed (e.g., you incorporate a sole proprietorship or form a partnership)[2]	Complete lines 1–16c (as applicable).
Purchased a going business[3]	Does not already have an EIN	Complete lines 1–16c (as applicable).
Created a trust	The trust is other than a grantor trust or an IRA trust[4]	Complete lines 1–16c (as applicable).
Created a pension plan as a plan administrator[5]	Needs an EIN for reporting purposes	Complete lines 1, 2, 4a–6, 8a, 9, and 16a–c.
Is a foreign person needing an EIN to comply with IRS withholding regulations	Needs an EIN to complete a Form W-8 (other than Form W-8ECI), avoid withholding on portfolio assets, or claim tax treaty benefits[6]	Complete lines 1–5b, 7a–b (SSN or ITIN optional), 8a–9, and 16a–c.
Is administering an estate	Needs an EIN to report estate income on Form 1041	Complete lines 1, 3, 4a–b, 8a, 9, and 16a–c.
Is a withholding agent for taxes on non-wage income paid to an alien (i.e., individual, corporation, or partnership, etc.)	Is an agent, broker, fiduciary, manager, tenant, or spouse who is required to file **Form 1042,** Annual Withholding Tax Return for U.S. Source Income of Foreign Persons	Complete lines 1, 2, 3 (if applicable), 4a–5b, 7a–b (if applicable), 8a, 9, and 16a–c.
Is a state or local agency	Serves as a tax reporting agent for public assistance recipients under Rev. Proc. 80-4, 1980-1 C.B. 581[7]	Complete lines 1, 2, 4a–5b, 8a, 9, and 16a–c.
Is a single-member LLC	Needs an EIN to file **Form 8832,** Classification Election, for filing employment tax returns, **or** for state reporting purposes[8]	Complete lines 1–16c (as applicable).
Is an S corporation	Needs an EIN to file **Form 2553,** Election by a Small Business Corporation[9]	Complete lines 1–16c (as applicable).

[1] For example, a sole proprietorship or self-employed farmer who establishes a qualified retirement plan, or is required to file excise, employment, alcohol, tobacco, or firearms returns, must have an EIN. **A partnership, corporation, REMIC (real estate mortgage investment conduit), nonprofit organization (church, club, etc.), or farmers' cooperative must use an EIN for any tax-related purpose even if the entity does not have employees.**

[2] However, **do not** apply for a new EIN if the existing entity only **(a)** changed its business name, **(b)** elected on Form 8832 to change the way it is taxed (or is covered by the default rules), or **(c)** terminated its partnership status because at least 50% of the total interests in partnership capital and profits were sold or exchanged within a 12-month period. (The EIN of the terminated partnership should continue to be used. See Regulations section 301.6109-1(d)(2)(iii).)

[3] Do not use the EIN of the prior business unless you became the "owner" of a corporation by acquiring its stock.

[4] However, IRA trusts that are required to file **Form 990-T,** Exempt Organization Business Income Tax Return, must have an EIN.

[5] A plan administrator is the person or group of persons specified as the administrator by the instrument under which the plan is operated.

[6] Entities applying to be a Qualified Intermediary (QI) need a QI-EIN even if they already have an EIN. **See Rev. Proc. 2000-12.**

[7] See also *Household employer* on page 4. **(Note:** State or local agencies may need an EIN for other reasons, e.g., hired employees.)

[8] Most LLCs **do not** need to file Form 8832. See **Limited liability company (LLC)** on page 4 for details on completing Form SS-4 for an LLC.

[9] An existing corporation that is electing or revoking S corporation status should use its previously-assigned EIN.

Instructions for Form SS-4

(Rev. December 2001)

Department of the Treasury
Internal Revenue Service

Application for Employer Identification Number

Section references are to the Internal Revenue Code unless otherwise noted.

General Instructions

Use these instructions to complete **Form SS-4,** Application for Employer Identification Number. Also see **Do I Need an EIN?** on page 2 of Form SS-4.

Purpose of Form

Use Form SS-4 to apply for an employer identification number (EIN). An EIN is a nine-digit number (for example, 12-3456789) assigned to sole proprietors, corporations, partnerships, estates, trusts, and other entities for tax filing and reporting purposes. The information you provide on this form will establish your business tax account.

 *An EIN is for use in connection with your business activities only. Do **not** use your EIN in place of your social security number (SSN).*

File only one Form SS-4. Generally, a sole proprietor should file only one Form SS-4 and needs only one EIN, regardless of the number of businesses operated as a sole proprietorship or trade names under which a business operates. However, if the proprietorship incorporates or enters into a partnership, a new EIN is required. Also, each corporation in an affiliated group must have its own EIN.

EIN applied for, but not received. If you do not have an EIN by the time a **return** is due, write "Applied For" and the date you applied in the space shown for the number. **Do not** show your social security number (SSN) as an EIN on returns.

If you do not have an EIN by the time a **tax deposit** is due, send your payment to the Internal Revenue Service Center for your filing area as shown in the instructions for the form that you are are filing. Make your check or money order payable to the **"United States Treasury"** and show your name (as shown on Form SS-4), address, type of tax, period covered, and date you applied for an EIN.

Related Forms and Publications

The following **forms** and **instructions** may be useful to filers of Form SS-4:
● **Form 990-T,** Exempt Organization Business Income Tax Return
● **Instructions for Form 990-T**
● **Schedule C (Form 1040),** Profit or Loss From Business
● **Schedule F (Form 1040),** Profit or Loss From Farming
● **Instructions for Form 1041 and Schedules A, B, D, G, I, J, and K-1,** U.S. Income Tax Return for Estates and Trusts

● **Form 1042,** Annual Withholding Tax Return for U.S. Source Income of Foreign Persons
● **Instructions for Form 1065,** U.S. Return of Partnership Income
● **Instructions for Form 1066,** U.S. Real Estate Mortgage Investment Conduit (REMIC) Income Tax Return
● **Instructions for Forms 1120 and 1120-A**
● **Form 2553,** Election by a Small Business Corporation
● **Form 2848,** Power of Attorney and Declaration of Representative
● **Form 8821,** Tax Information Authorization
● **Form 8832,** Entity Classification Election

For more **information** about filing Form SS-4 and related issues, see:
● **Circular A,** Agricultural Employer's Tax Guide (Pub. 51)
● **Circular E,** Employer's Tax Guide (Pub. 15)
● **Pub. 538,** Accounting Periods and Methods
● **Pub. 542,** Corporations
● **Pub. 557,** Exempt Status for Your Organization
● **Pub. 583,** Starting a Business and Keeping Records
● **Pub. 966,** EFTPS: Now a Full Range of Electronic Choices to Pay All Your Federal Taxes
● **Pub. 1635,** Understanding Your EIN
● **Package 1023,** Application for Recognition of Exemption
● **Package 1024,** Application for Recognition of Exemption Under Section 501(a)

How To Get Forms and Publications

Phone. You can order forms, instructions, and publications by phone 24 hours a day, 7 days a week. Just call 1-800-TAX-FORM (1-800-829-3676). You should receive your order or notification of its status within 10 workdays.

Personal computer. With your personal computer and modem, you can get the forms and information you need using the IRS Web Site at **www.irs.gov** or File Transfer Protocol at **ftp.irs.gov.**

CD-ROM. For small businesses, return preparers, or others who may frequently need tax forms or publications, a CD-ROM containing over 2,000 tax products (including many prior year forms) can be purchased from the National Technical Information Service (NTIS).

To order **Pub. 1796,** Federal Tax Products on CD-ROM, call **1-877-CDFORMS** (1-877-233-6767) toll free or connect to **www.irs.gov/cdorders.**

Cat. No. 62736F

Tax Help for Your Business

IRS-sponsored Small Business Workshops provide information about your Federal and state tax obligations. For information about workshops in your area, call 1-800-829-1040 and ask for your Taxpayer Education Coordinator.

How To Apply

You can apply for an EIN by telephone, fax, or mail depending on how soon you need to use the EIN.

Application by Tele-TIN. Under the Tele-TIN program, you can receive your EIN by telephone and use it immediately to file a return or make a payment. To receive an EIN by telephone, IRS suggests that you complete Form SS-4 so that you will have all relevant information available. Then call the Tele-TIN number at 1-866-816-2065. (International applicants must call 215-516-6999.) Tele-TIN hours of operation are 7:30 a.m. to 5:30 p.m. The person making the call must be authorized to sign the form or be an authorized designee. See **Signature** and **Third Party Designee** on page 6. Also see the **TIP** below.

An IRS representative will use the information from the Form SS-4 to establish your account and assign you an EIN. Write the number you are given on the upper right corner of the form and sign and date it. Keep this copy for your records.

If requested by an IRS representative, mail or fax (facsimile) the signed Form SS-4 (including any Third Party Designee authorization) **within 24 hours** to the Tele-TIN Unit at the service center address provided by the IRS representative.

TIP *Taxpayer representatives can use Tele-TIN to apply for an EIN on behalf of their client and request that the EIN be faxed to their **client** on the same day. (**Note:** By utilizing this procedure, you are authorizing the IRS to fax the EIN without a cover sheet.)*

Application by Fax-TIN. Under the Fax-TIN program, you can receive your EIN by fax within 4 business days. Complete and fax Form SS-4 to the IRS using the Fax-TIN number listed below for your state. A long-distance charge to callers outside of the local calling area will apply. Fax-TIN numbers can only be used to apply for an EIN. **The numbers may change without notice.** Fax-TIN is available 24 hours a day, 7 days a week.

Be sure to provide your fax number so that IRS can fax the EIN back to you. (**Note:** By utilizing this procedure, you are authorizing the IRS to fax the EIN without a cover sheet.)

Do not call Tele-TIN for the same entity because duplicate EINs may be issued. See **Third Party Designee** on page 6.

Application by mail. Complete Form SS-4 at least 4 to 5 weeks before you will need an EIN. Sign and date the application and mail it to the service center address for your state. You will receive your EIN in the mail in approximately 4 weeks. See also **Third Party Designee** on page 6.

Call 1-800-829-1040 to verify a number or to ask about the status of an application by mail.

If your principal business, office or agency, or legal residence in the case of an individual, is located in:	Call the Tele-TIN or Fax-TIN number shown or file with the "Internal Revenue Service Center" at:
Connecticut, Delaware, District of Columbia, Florida, Georgia, Maine, Maryland, Massachusetts, New Hampshire, New Jersey, New York, North Carolina, Ohio, Pennsylvania, Rhode Island, South Carolina, Vermont, Virginia, West Virginia	Attn: EIN Operation Holtsville, NY 00501 Tele-TIN 866-816-2065 Fax-TIN 631-447-8960
Illinois, Indiana, Kentucky, Michigan	Attn: EIN Operation Cincinnati, OH 45999 Tele-TIN 866-816-2065 Fax-TIN 859-669-5760
Alabama, Alaska, Arizona, Arkansas, California, Colorado, Hawaii, Idaho, Iowa, Kansas, Louisiana, Minnesota, Mississippi, Missouri, Montana, Nebraska, Nevada, New Mexico, North Dakota, Oklahoma, Oregon, Puerto Rico, South Dakota, Tennessee, Texas, Utah, Washington, Wisconsin, Wyoming	Attn: EIN Operation Philadelphia, PA 19255 Tele-TIN 866-816-2065 Fax-TIN 215-516-3990
If you have no legal residence, principal place of business, or principal office or agency in any state:	Attn: EIN Operation Philadelphia, PA 19255 Tele-TIN 215-516-6999 Fax-TIN 215-516-3990

Specific Instructions

Print or type all entries on Form SS-4. Follow the instructions for each line to expedite processing and to avoid unnecessary IRS requests for additional information. Enter "N/A" (nonapplicable) on the lines that do not apply.

Line 1—Legal name of entity (or individual) for whom the EIN is being requested. Enter the legal name of the entity (or individual) applying for the EIN exactly as it appears on the social security card, charter, or other applicable legal document.

Individuals. Enter your first name, middle initial, and last name. If you are a sole proprietor, enter your individual name, not your business name. Enter your business name on line 2. Do not use abbreviations or nicknames on line 1.

Trusts. Enter the name of the trust.

Estate of a decedent. Enter the name of the estate.

Partnerships. Enter the legal name of the partnership as it appears in the partnership agreement.

Do Not Staple   6969

Form **1096** Department of the Treasury Internal Revenue Service	**Annual Summary and Transmittal of** **U.S. Information Returns**	OMB No. 1545-0108 **2002**

┌─ FILER'S name ─────────────────────────────┐

  Street address (including room or suite number)

  City, state, and ZIP code
└──┘

Name of person to contact	Telephone number ( )	**For Official Use Only**
Fax number ( )	E-mail address	☐☐☐☐☐☐ ☐☐

1 Employer identification number	**2** Social security number	**3** Total number of forms	**4** Federal income tax withheld $	**5** Total amount reported with this Form 1096 $

Enter an "X" in only one box below to indicate the type of form being filed.   If this is your **final return**, enter an "X" here . . . ▶ ☐

W-2G 32	1098 81	1098-E 84	1098-T 83	1099-A 80	1099-B 79	1099-C 85	1099-DIV 91	1099-G 86	1099-INT 92	1099-LTC 93	1099-MISC 95	1099-MSA 94	1099-OID 96
☐	☐	☐	☐	☐	☐	☐	☐	☐	☐	☐	☐	☐	☐

1099-PATR 97	1099-Q 31	1099-R 98	1099-S 75	5498 28	5498-MSA 27
☐	☐	☐	☐	☐	☐

Please return this entire page to the Internal Revenue Service. Photocopies are not acceptable.

Under penalties of perjury, I declare that I have examined this return and accompanying documents, and, to the best of my knowledge and belief, they are true, correct, and complete.

Signature ▶   Title ▶   Date ▶

Instructions

Purpose of form. Use this form to transmit paper Forms 1099, 1098, 5498, and W-2G to the Internal Revenue Service. **Do not use Form 1096 to transmit magnetic media.** See **Form 4804,** Transmittal of Information Returns Reported Magnetically.

Who must file. The name, address, and TIN of the filer on this form must be the same as those you enter in the upper left area of Form 1099, 1098, 5498, or W-2G. A filer includes a payer, a recipient of mortgage interest payments (including points) or student loan interest, an educational institution, a broker, a barter exchange, a creditor, a person reporting real estate transactions, a trustee or issuer of any individual retirement arrangement or an Archer MSA (including a Medicare+Choice MSA), and a lender who acquires an interest in secured property or who has reason to know that the property has been abandoned.

Preaddressed Form 1096. If you received a preaddressed Form 1096 from the IRS with Package 1099, use it to transmit paper Forms 1099, 1098, 5498, and W-2G to the Internal Revenue Service. If any of the imprinted information is incorrect, make corrections on the form.

Note: *You will no longer receive an IRS-prepared label with your Package 1099.*

If you are not using a preaddressed form, enter the filer's name, address (including room, suite, or other unit number), and TIN in the spaces provided on the form.

When to file. File Form 1096 with Forms 1099, 1098, or W-2G by February 28, 2003. File Form 1096 with Forms 5498 by June 2, 2003.

Where To File

Send all information returns filed on paper with Form 1096 to the following:

If your principal business, office or agency, or legal residence in the case of an individual, is located in ▼	Use the following Internal Revenue Service Center address ▼
Alabama, Arizona, Florida, Georgia, Louisiana, Mississippi, New Mexico, North Carolina, Texas, Virginia	Austin, TX 73301
Arkansas, Connecticut, Delaware, Kentucky, Maine, Massachusetts, New Hampshire, New Jersey, New York, Ohio, Pennsylvania, Rhode Island, Vermont, West Virginia	Cincinnati, OH 45999
Illinois, Indiana, Iowa, Kansas, Michigan, Minnesota, Missouri, Nebraska, North Dakota, Oklahoma, South Carolina, South Dakota, Tennessee, Wisconsin	Kansas City, MO 64999

For more information and the Privacy Act and Paperwork Reduction Act Notice, see the 2002 General Instructions for Forms 1099, 1098, 5498, and W-2G.   Cat. No. 14400O   Form **1096** (2002)

Alaska, California, Colorado, District of Columbia, Hawaii, Idaho, Maryland, Montana, Nevada, Oregon, Utah, Washington, Wyoming	Ogden, UT 84201

If your legal residence or principal place of business is outside the United States, file with the Internal Revenue Service Center, Cincinnati, OH 45999.

Transmitting to the IRS. Send the forms in a flat mailing (not folded). Group the forms by form number and transmit each group with a **separate** Form 1096. For example, if you must file both Forms 1098 and 1099-A, complete one Form 1096 to transmit your Forms 1098 and another Form 1096 to transmit your Forms 1099-A. You need not submit original and corrected returns separately. **Do not** send a form (1099, 5498, etc.) containing summary (subtotal) information with Form 1096. Summary information for the group of forms being sent is entered only in boxes 3, 4, and 5 of Form 1096.

Box 1 or 2. Complete only if you are not using a preaddressed Form 1096. Make an entry in **either** box 1 or 2; not both. Individuals not in a trade or business must enter their social security number (SSN) in box 2; sole proprietors and all others must enter their employer identification number (EIN) in box 1. However, sole proprietors who do not have an EIN must enter their SSN in box 2. Use the same EIN or SSN on Form 1096 that you use on Form 1099, 1098, 5498, or W-2G.

Box 3. Enter the number of forms you are transmitting with this Form 1096. Do not include blank or voided forms or the Form 1096 in your total. Enter the number of correctly completed forms, not the number of pages, being transmitted. For example, if you send one page of three-to-a-page Forms 5498 with a Form 1096 and you have correctly completed two Forms 5498 on that page, enter "2" in box 3 of Form 1096.

Box 4. Enter the total Federal income tax withheld shown on the forms being transmitted with this Form 1096.

Box 5. No entry is required if you are filing Forms 1098-T, 1099-A, or 1099-G. For all other forms, enter the total of the amounts from the specific boxes of the forms listed below:

Form W-2G	Box 1
Form 1098	Boxes 1 and 2
Form 1098-E	Box 1
Form 1099-B	Boxes 2 and 3
Form 1099-C	Box 2
Form 1099-DIV	Boxes 1, 2a, 3, 8, and 9
Form 1099-INT	Boxes 1 and 3
Form 1099-LTC	Boxes 1 and 2
Form 1099-MISC	Boxes 1, 2, 3, 5, 6, 7, 8, 10, 13, and 14
Form 1099-MSA	Box 1
Form 1099-OID	Boxes 1, 2, and 6
Form 1099-PATR	Boxes 1, 2, 3, and 5
Form 1099-Q	Box 2
Form 1099-R	Box 1
Form 1099-S	Box 2
Form 5498	Boxes 1, 2, 3, 4, 5, 8, 9, 10, and 11
Form 5498-MSA	Box 1

Final return. If you will not be required to file Forms 1099, 1098, 5498, or W-2G in the future, either on paper, on magnetic media, or electronically, enter an "X" in the "**final return**" box.

Type of form. Enter an "X" in the appropriate box to indicate the type of form you are transmitting.

Corrected returns. For information about filing corrections, see the **2002 General Instructions for Forms 1099, 1098, 5498, and W-2G.** Originals and corrections of the same type of return can be submitted using one Form 1096.

9595 ☐ VOID ☐ CORRECTED

| PAYER'S name, street address, city, state, ZIP code, and telephone no. | **1** Rents $ | OMB No. 1545-0115 | **Miscellaneous Income** |
| | **2** Royalties $ | **2002** Form **1099-MISC** | |

	3 Other income $	**4** Federal income tax withheld $	**Copy A**
PAYER'S Federal identification number / RECIPIENT'S identification number	**5** Fishing boat proceeds $	**6** Medical and health care payments $	**For Internal Revenue Service Center**
			File with Form 1096.
RECIPIENT'S name	**7** Nonemployee compensation $	**8** Substitute payments in lieu of dividends or interest $	For Privacy Act and Paperwork Reduction Act Notice, see the **2002 General Instructions for Forms 1099, 1098, 5498, and W-2G.**
Street address (including apt. no.)	**9** Payer made direct sales of $5,000 or more of consumer products to a buyer (recipient) for resale ▶ ☐	**10** Crop insurance proceeds $	
City, state, and ZIP code	**11** ///////	**12** ///////	
Account number (optional) 2nd TIN not. ☐	**13** Excess golden parachute payments $	**14** Gross proceeds paid to an attorney $	
15	**16** State tax withheld $ $	**17** State/Payer's state no.	**18** State income $ $

Form **1099-MISC**   Cat. No. 14425J   Department of the Treasury - Internal Revenue Service

Do Not Cut or Separate Forms on This Page — Do Not Cut or Separate Forms on This Page

Instructions for Payers

We now provide general and specific form instructions as separate products. The products you should use for 2002 are the **General Instructions for Forms 1099, 1098, 5498, and W-2G** and the separate specific instructions for each information return you file. Specific information needed to complete this form is given in the **2002 Instructions for Form 1099-MISC.** A chart in the general instructions gives a quick guide to which form must be filed to report a particular payment. To order these instructions and additional forms, call 1-800-TAX-FORM (1-800-829-3676).

Caution: *Because the IRS processes paper forms by machine (optical character recognition equipment), you cannot file with the IRS Forms 1096, 1098, 1099, or 5498 that you print from the IRS Web Site.*

Due dates. Furnish Copy B of this form to the recipient by January 31, 2003.

File Copy A of this form with the IRS by February 28, 2003. If you file electronically, the due date is March 31, 2003.

Managing a Professional Print Job

Professional printers can do business cards, brochures, fliers, and many other type of print jobs. A recommendation is to use a professional printer to create your business cards, but use pre-printed paper and your own office equipment (or your local copy center) to create your brochures, fliers, and introductory letters.

Categories of Printers

Printers can be grouped into four categories, which also roughly reflects their pricing from least expensive to most expensive:

- Copy centers that typically contract print jobs to printers (for example, Kinko's, Lazerquick)

- Small printers that target quick turn-around, low-volume jobs like newsletters and simple business cards (for example, Sudden Printing, Minuteman Press)

- Mid-sized printers might have four- or five-color presses and do runs of 10,000 and fewer.

- Large printers will have four- and five-color presses and offer specialty services in-house (binding, embossing, etc). These businesses usually specialize in larger quantity runs, as the setup time is longer and therefore more expensive.

Printer Selection

1. Ask around to get recommendations regarding local printers.

2. Contact at least three different printers to schedule a meeting to talk about your print job.

3. Meet the printer and find out if they have a specific printing niche. Often, they will give you a tour of their facility. How busy are they? How clean is their shop? Do the personnel seem professional and knowledgeable?

4. Ask to see samples of their work. When looking at the samples, make sure to check out these details:

- Ink coverage – is it even? There shouldn't be any little specks or white spots.

- Folds – Are they nicely scored, folded and cut parallel? There shouldn't be any cracking, uneven edges, or sloppy folds.

- How are their special treatments? Most printers will subcontract these steps. Look for smooth embossing and foils that fit nicely within the printed areas.

5. Show them the color printout of your design so they can see what the job looks like.

6. Leave them a copy of the print spec sheet, including your desired print quantities.

7. Get job quotes from several (three to five) printers. Compare the quotes.

8. Evaluate the printers on the quality of work, cost, and timeliness such as, can they meet your schedule? Plus, how do you personally feel about the print rep you worked with? It's important to get a printer that you can trust and work with.

9. Once you've chosen your printer, submit your order. Typically you will have to pay half the cost up front and the rest on delivery.

The Print Process

Once you've chosen the printer and submitted the order, your job shifts to one of quality control and approval. There are several points during the print process where you need to review and approve the work before the printer can go to the next step. Below is a description of the print process, along with the various approval milestones.

1. Drop off the disk and color printout with your selected printer.

2. Ask what the tentative schedule will be (it always changes, but it should be close). Let the printer know if there are specific days that you will be out of town or unreachable. There are two approval steps where you'll be needed, one of which occurs the day of the printing.

3. The printer will call you when "bluelines" are ready to check. A blueline is literally a light blue version of what will be printed.

4. Check the blueline for correctness:

- Is everything in the correct spot?

- Are the fonts the correct ones and the right size?

- Do the pieces of your logo fit nicely without white spaces or overlap (these would show up as a dark color)?

- Look for any specks that shouldn't be there. Everything on the blueline will show up on your printed piece (except it will be in your chosen colors). Circle anything that looks suspicious, talk to the printer to have the error fixed before it goes to print.

5. The next step is the press check. Typically, the printer will call you the day before to give you a rough idea of when the job will go to print. (Confirm this with the printer when you check the bluelines.) They'll call you 30 to 60 minutes before it goes on the press so you can review and approve the artwork. If you travel, you will need to coordinate your schedule with the printer's schedule.

6. At a press check look for:

- Are all the elements there?

- Are all the elements in the right place?

- Are the colors correct? Match them to your color chips. (You should get these when you place your order.)

- Are the printed colors smooth and solid?

- Make sure there is no ink where it shouldn't be.

7. Once you've approved the press check, you will be asked to sign a press sheet. Your signature indicates that you have reviewed the press check and given your approval to run the job. You are responsible for catching any errors. Once you approve the job, you are liable for the cost.

8. After you have approved the press check, it typically takes a couple of days for the job to run, dry, and get trimmed. If you are going to have your cards embossed, add a few more days for that step.

9. The printer should call you when the cards are ready to be picked up. When you pick the cards up, you will need to pay the remaining amount.

About the Author

Dorcas Kelley CPCC CMC is founder of Clarity In Action, a business and personal coaching practice for high achievers who want to aggressively get beyond obstacles and reach their goals. Through the coaching process, her clients develop greater clarity, focus, and an increased capacity for effective action.

She is also founder and president of Kelley-Naumchik Consulting LLC, a management consulting firm that works with organizations of all sizes to dramatically improve the way they do business and achieve breakthrough results.
A successful entrepreneur, she has owned her businesses since 1994. Prior to that, Dorcas worked for Hewlett-Packard Company as an internal consultant and coach, and for Arthur Andersen Consulting.

Dorcas draws on a wealth of private and public sector expertise. She has always been a motivator of people and a model of high achievement for others, including her clients. She coaches executives, business owners, professionals, entrepreneurs, individuals, and other coaches to reach the next level of success in their business and personal lives. Additionally, she has delivered numerous workshops and seminars on a wide range of topics.

A member of Phi Beta Kappa, Dorcas' credentials include an MBA with High Honors from UC Los Angeles and a BA with Highest Honors in Sociology from UC Santa Barbara. She completed her coach training and certification through The Coaches Training Institute in San Rafael, California, and is a Certified Professional Co-Active Coach.

Dorcas is a member of the International Coach Federation and a co-host of the Monterey Bay (California) Chapter. She is also a member of the Institute of Management Consultants and a Certified Management Consultant. She is also on the board of directors for the Northern California chapter of IMC. She is a co-founder of the Monterey Bay Consultants Group, and belongs to the Salinas Valley Chamber of Commerce, the Junior League of Monterey County, the National Association for Female Executives, and the American Business Women's Association.

Dorcas lives in the Monterey Bay area of Northern California with her husband Chris, four cats, three dogs, two goats, and a sheep named Laverne.

Do You Have Questions or Feedback?
I'd like to hear from you!

I welcome any constructive feedback or suggestions for the next edition.
If you have a question, I'll try to reply in a timely fashion.
Your question may be selected to be featured in my monthly email newsletter
"The Business of Coaching." If you would like to subscribe to this email
newsletter, please visit my website at www.thebusinessofcoaching.com. Or, feel
free to email me at the following address.

Please send email to:
dorcask@clarityinaction.com

Please visit my websites at:
www.clarityinaction.com
www.thebusinessofcoaching.com

I Wish You Success
and Good Fortune
in Your Business Adventure!

Quick Order Form

Secure Internet Orders: www.thebusinessofcoaching.com

Fax Orders: 831-769-9035. Fax this form and credit card info.

Postal Orders: Clarity in Action; 19250 Reavis Way, Salinas CA 93907. 831-663-5364. Send this form along with your payment.

Please send me more information on:

Free Newsletter   Free Teleclasses   Speaking / Seminars
Coach Mentoring   Personal Coaching   Free Sample Session

Name:

Address:

City: State :   Zip:

Telephone:

email address:

The Business of Coaching

- Bookset (book and workbook): $38.90
- Add 7.25% sales tax for shipments to California addresses ($2.82)
- Shipping: $4 (7-10 business days US); $7 (3-5 business days US); $13 (Fed Ex 2nd day US); $9 (Canada); $15 (other International)

Payment

Check#   Credit Card: Visa   Mastercard   American Express

Card number:

Name on card:

Expiration date:

ClarityInAction.com

Bringing vision and action together!

TheBusinessOfCoaching.com

Passionate about the success of your life & your business!